Verbal Reasoning
& Comprehension
The 11+
10-Minute Tests

For the CEM (Durham University) test

Ages
8-9

Practise • Prepare • Pass
Everything your child needs for 11+ success

How to use this book

This book is made up of 10-minute tests and puzzle pages.
There are answers and detailed explanations in the pull-out section at the back of the book.

10-Minute Tests

- There are 31 tests in this book, each containing either 20 or 26 questions.

- Each test is designed to cover a good range of the question styles and topics that
  your child could come across in the verbal reasoning section of their 11+ test.

- Your child should aim to score around 17 out of 20 or 22 out of 26 in each of the 10-minute tests.
  If they score less than this, use their results to work out the areas they need more practice on.

- If your child hasn't managed to finish the test in time, they need to work on increasing their
  speed, whereas if they have made a lot of mistakes, they need to work more carefully.

- Keep track of your child's scores using the progress chart on the inside back cover of the book.

Puzzle Pages

- There are 10 puzzle pages in this book. The puzzles are a great break from test preparation.
  They also encourage children to practise the same skills that they will need in the test,
  but in a fun way.

Published by CGP

Editors:
Marc Barnard, Alex Fairer, Holly Robinson

With thanks to Matt Topping and Judy Hornigold for the proofreading.
With thanks to Jan Greenway for the copyright research.

Please note that CGP is not associated with CEM or The University of Durham in any way.
This book does not include any official questions and it is not endorsed by CEM or The University of Durham.
CEM, Centre for Evaluation and Monitoring, Durham University and *The University of Durham*
are all trademarks of The University of Durham.

ISBN: 978 1 78294 774 5
Printed by Elanders Ltd, Newcastle upon Tyne
Clipart from Corel®

Based on the classic CGP style created by Richard Parsons.

Contents

You have **10 minutes** to do this test. Work as quickly and as accurately as you can.

Read this passage carefully and answer the questions that follow.

An adapted extract from 'Cast Upon the Breakers'

Rodney was satisfied with his job as landlord* of the Miners' Rest. His pay was good and he was able to save a large amount of money each month, but he worked long hours and spent most of his time indoors. After three months there, he was starting to show his exhaustion. When his good friend and owner of the pub,

5 Pettigrew, saw him, he said, "Rodney, you look shattered. You need a change."

"Does that mean you're going to fire me?" asked Rodney, with a smile.

"It means that I am going to give you a holiday."

"But what would I do if I took a holiday? I wouldn't like to lounge around with nothing to do."

10 "That kind of holiday wouldn't do you any good. I'll tell you the plan. I own a small mine in Babcock, about fifty miles north of Oreville. I will send you up to examine it, and report back to me. Can you ride a horse?"

"Yes."

"Good, because that's the only way you can get there. There are no trains in that

15 direction, nor any other way of travel except on foot or on horseback. A long ride like that with plenty of fresh air will do you good. What do you say?"

"I would like nothing better," replied Rodney, with his eyes sparkling. "Only, what will you do without me?"

"I employ a man in the mines who will do part of your work, and I will keep an

20 eye on things. There's no need to worry about that. Do you think you can find your way?"

"Give me the general direction, and I will make sure I do so. When should I start?"

"Day after tomorrow. That will give me a day to arrange everything."

*landlord — *a person who runs a pub*

Horatio Alger Jr.

Answer these questions about the text that you've just read.
Circle the letter that matches the correct answer.

1. What reason does Rodney have for being happy with his job?

   A   His hours are long.

   B   His employer is giving him a holiday.

   C   He is well paid.

   D   He had always wanted to be a landlord.

2. How is Rodney going to travel to the mine in Babcock?

   A   By rail

   B   On foot

   C   By aeroplane

   D   On horseback

3. Line 17 describes Rodney's eyes as "sparkling". This suggests:

   A   Rodney is pleased.

   B   Rodney is confused.

   C   Rodney is angry.

   D   Rodney is beautiful.

4. Who will act as landlord of the Miners' Rest while Rodney is away?

   A   Someone who is currently working there

   B   No-one

   C   Pettigrew is going to advertise for a new employee.

   D   A man who works for Pettigrew in the mines

5. According to the text, why is Rodney going to the mines the "Day after tomorrow" (line 24)?

    A   To give him time to get to Babcock

    B   To give Pettigrew time to sort things out

    C   To give him time to say goodbye

    D   Because he has to work at the Miners' Rest the next day

6. What does the word "exhaustion" (line 4) mean?

    A   Collapse

    B   Tiredness

    C   Enthusiasm

    D   Irritation

7. What does the word "examine" (line 12) mean?

    A   Inspect

    B   Allow

    C   Watch

    D   Mark

Rearrange the words so that each sentence makes sense. Underline the word which doesn't fit into the sentence.

Example: to I have <u>lamp</u> room my tidy

8. mud boots got I <u>spend</u> my on

9. loudly Ruth slurped banana <u>oranges</u> her smoothie

10. could to <u>flying</u> Tom not wait Japan visit

11. asked a <u>supermarket</u> for directions woman I

12. are <u>eating</u> we to a restaurant tomorrow going

13. on floor dropped teapot Hillary <u>smashing</u> the the

14. found my underground <u>slobbers</u> dog a bone

> Underline the word below that means the opposite,
> or nearly the opposite, of the word on the left.
>
> **Example: ill**   nice   <u>well</u>   sick   happy

15. **brilliant**   wonderful   <u>awful</u>   normal   annoying

16. **beaming**   grinning   <u>scowling</u>   laughing   shrugging

17. **hasty**   <u>slow</u>   busy   neatly   noisy

18. **clear**   transparent   <u>murky</u>   bright   certain

19. **all**   lots   many   <u>none</u>   some

20. **bellow**   <u>quiet</u>   shout   frown   whisper

END OF TEST

/ 20

You have **10 minutes** to do this test. Work as quickly and as accurately as you can.

Fill in the missing letters to complete the words in the following passage.

1. The Victorian era was a t i m e of great scientific achievement. In order

2. to share and celebrate these advances, Britain o r g a n i s e d an

3. exhibition. Countries from all over the w o r l d were given space to

4. show off their achievements. The exhibition was h e l d in a huge glass

5. and iron building c a l l e d the Crystal Palace. This was the first time

6. so many countries had come together in one p l a c e. Six million

7. people visited the exhibition. Many were o r d i n a r y people

    who had travelled on a train for the first time to get there.

8. When the exhibition f i n i s h e d, the Crystal Palace was rebuilt

9. in South London. This was incredibly e x p e n s i v e and the

10. Palace was declared bankrupt in 1911. In 1936, a fire s w e p t through

11. the Palace, destroying it. Although the Palace no longer e x i s t s,

12. the area where it used to s t a n d is now called 'Crystal Palace'.

6

Complete the word on the right so that it means the opposite, or nearly the opposite, of the word on the left.

Example: strong [w][e][a][k]

13. frozen   [m][e][l][t][e][d]

14. clothed   [n][a][k][e][d]

15. blunt   [s][h][a][r][p]

16. thorough   [c][a][r][e][l][e][s][s]

17. unique   [n][o][r][m][a][l]

Four of the words in each list are linked. Underline the word that is **not** related to the other four.

Example: cow   hen   sheep   pig   <u>monkey</u>

18. peek   glimpse   peep   <u>stare</u>   glance

19. grimy   dingy   drab   dreary   <u>decent</u>

20. <u>ear</u>   nose   beak   snout   trunk

21. chess   <u>yo-yo</u>   cards   draughts   dominoes

22. thief   <u>crime</u>   burglar   pickpocket   robber

Rearrange the words so that each sentence makes sense. Underline the word which doesn't fit into the sentence.

Example: to I have <u>lamp</u> room my tidy

23. a is <u>art</u> painter Chloe talented very

24. bubble herself bath a Linda <u>relax</u> ran

25. fox its hid <u>run</u> in the burrow

26. went on <u>sail</u> Harriet sailing lake the

END OF TEST

/ 26

You have **10 minutes** to do this test. Work as quickly and as accurately as you can.

Choose the correct words to complete the passage below.

1. ☑ rainforests
   ☐ northern
   ☐ parts

Native to the _____ of South America, capybaras are the world's

2. ☐ enormous
   ☐ unusual
   ☑ largest

rodent. They usually live near rivers and spend much of their time

3. ☐ sheltered
   ☐ eat
   ☑ escape

swimming. They use the water to _____ from predators, but go onto land to

4. ☑ help
   ☐ manage
   ☐ swim

rest. They have webbed feet to _____ them travel through the water. They live

5. ☐ food
   ☑ diet
   ☐ eating

on a _____ of grass and aquatic plants. Capybaras are very social and live in

6. ☐ towns
   ☑ groups
   ☐ family

of up to twenty. They make barking

7. ☑ noises
   ☐ loudly
   ☐ noisy

to communicate and

8. ☐ since
   ☐ feeding
   ☑ around

are mostly active _____ sunrise and sunset. Capybaras are

9. ☐ never
   ☑ endangered
   ☑ quite

common and can be found in most South American countries. They are a favourite

prey of many animals
10. ☐ like
☐ including as jaguars, anacondas and pumas. Humans
☑ such

11. ☑ hunt
also   ☐ eaten   capybaras for their fur and meat, and it's
☐ farming

12. ☐ agreeing
☐ allowing   in
☑ traditional

Venezuela to eat capybara before Easter.

> The words on the left are related in some way. Choose the word from the
> brackets that fits best with the words on the left.
>
> **Example**: **car bus ferry coach** (road drive <u>train</u> cargo journey)

13. **florist butcher's grocer's bookshop** (library <u>bakery</u> bank park museum)

14. **cotton satin silk felt** (material wood clothes <u>wool</u> fabric)

15. **tin copper aluminium iron** (metal plastic <u>steel</u> glass foil)

16. **fight brawl clash bicker** (anger weep <u>squabble</u> annoy confront)

17. **backpack satchel handbag briefcase** (wallet <u>rucksack</u> pocket box crate)

Complete the word on the right so that it means the same, or nearly the same, as the word on the left.

Example: foe e n e m y

18. chirp t w e e t

19. collision c r a s h

20. cruel v i c i o u s

21. bent c r o o k e d

Four of the words in each list are linked. Underline the word that is **not** related to the other four.

Example: cow   hen   sheep   pig   monkey

22. toss   hurl   throw   drop   fling

23. liver   kidney   foot   heart   stomach

24. cloak   shawl   cape   shorts   cardigan

25. stumble   trip   prance   stagger   slip

26. tin   jar   bowl   can   packet

END OF TEST

/ 26

Test 3

Time for a break! This puzzle is a great way to practise your **word-making** skills.

Troll Trouble

Princess Clara has been kidnapped by a troll. The troll made her write a letter to her family. But in some words, she removed or added letters to give clues to her location. Write down each missing letter and each extra letter in the box below. Then unjumble them on the lines to reveal her location — you can use the map of the kingdom to help you.

> Dear famly,
>
> I have been kinapped by a troll and he has take me to his secret lair. I am looking on the bright side of things thogh — the views are terible, but at leaset I can go swimmin wenever I like. The troll says that if you give him a chest of gold, he will sett me free. If you refuse, you will never seee me again. You hav a week to decidde. Please hury up and pay — being kidnapped is a bit rubish.
>
> Love,
> Princess Clara

~~dritteg~~ ted e r b

u n d e r   t h e   b r i d g e

You have **10 minutes** to do this test. Work as quickly and as accurately as you can.

Read this poem carefully and answer the questions that follow.

The Echoing Green

"The Echoing Green" is a poem about a small field where children play.

The sun does arise,
And make happy the skies.
The merry bells ring
To welcome the spring.
5   The sky-lark and thrush,
The birds of the bush,
Sing louder around,
To the bells' cheerful sound.
While our sports shall be seen
10 On the Echoing Green.

Old John, with white hair
Does laugh away care,
Sitting under the oak,
Among the old folk,
15 They laugh at our play,
And soon they all say.
'Such, such were the joys.
When we all girls and boys,
In our youth-time were seen,
20 On the Echoing Green.'
Till the little ones weary

No more can be merry
The sun does descend,
And our sports have an end:
25 Round the laps of their mothers,
Many sisters and brothers,
Like birds in their nest,
Are ready for rest;
And sport no more seen,
30 On the darkening Green.

William Blake

Answer these questions about the text that you've just read.
Circle the letter that matches the correct answer.

1. According to the narrator, why are the bells ringing in line 3?

    A   There's a wedding taking place.

    B   It's midday.

    C   It's spring.

    D   It's sunny.

2. Which word best describes how the "old folk" are feeling in lines 16-20?

    A   Tired

    B   Irritated

    C   Happy

    D   Excited

3. In lines 21-22, why do the children stop being "merry"?

    A   They are bored.

    B   They are too tired.

    C   They have been told to stop playing.

    D   It's too cold.

4. Which of the following is not mentioned in the text?

    A   Which sounds can be heard

    B   The colour of Old John's hair

    C   Which sports the children are playing

    D   Which types of birds are singing

5. Over what period of time does the poem take place?

    A   One year

    B   Spring

    C   Four hours

    D   One day

6. What does "cheerful" (line 8) mean?

    A   Tired

    B   Joyful

    C   Familiar

    D   Noisy

7. What does "descend" (line 23) mean?

    A   Go down

    B   Go up

    C   Move across

    D   Fall over

The words on the left are related in some way. Choose the word from the brackets that fits best with the words on the left.

  Example: **car bus ferry coach** (road drive <u>train</u> cargo journey)

---

8. **enormous huge gigantic titanic** (tiny colossal wide minute imaginary)

9. **neigh woof bleat miaow** (rustle sniff croak sigh twang)

10. **blazer jumper jacket coat** (gloves vest sweatshirt jeans socks)

11. **ton ounce pound kilogram** (foot kilometre weight litre gram)

12. **sweet bitter delicious sour** (tasty food seasoning sugar grilled)

13. **closet cabinet wardrobe chest** (storage cupboard home room table)

14. **grapefruit lemon orange lime** (apple tangerine citrus cherry fruit)

Complete the word on the right so that it means the opposite,
or nearly the opposite, of the word on the left.

Example: strong   ⬚w⬚⬚e⬚⬚a⬚⬚k⬚

15. present   ⬚a⬚⬚b⬚⬚ ⬚⬚e⬚⬚ ⬚⬚t⬚

16. dusk   ⬚ ⬚⬚a⬚⬚w⬚⬚ ⬚

17. bore   ⬚ ⬚⬚m⬚⬚u⬚⬚ ⬚⬚e⬚

18. wealth   ⬚ ⬚⬚o⬚⬚v⬚⬚ ⬚⬚r⬚⬚t⬚⬚ ⬚

19. plenty   ⬚ ⬚⬚ ⬚⬚c⬚⬚k⬚

20. centre   ⬚ ⬚⬚d⬚⬚g⬚⬚ ⬚

END OF TEST

/ 20

You have **10 minutes** to do this test. Work as quickly and as accurately as you can.

Fill in the missing letters to complete the words in the following passage.

1.   Most people are a w ☐ ☐ e of Florence Nightingale and her

2.   ☐ ☐ r k improving conditions in hospitals. Less well-known is Mary

3.   Seacole, who also worked d ☐ r ☐ n g the Crimean War as a nurse.

4.   Born in Jamaica to a Scottish ☐ a ☐ h e r and a Jamaican mother, she

5.   had a good ☐ d u ☐ a ☐ ☐ o n and learnt about traditional

6.   Jamaican m e ☐ i c ☐ n e from her mother. She gained a

7.   reputation as a skilled nurse and w ☐ n t ☐ ☐ to go to Crimea

8.   with Florence Nightingale's t ☐ ☐ m of nurses, but her application was

9.   u ☐ s u c ☐ e ☐ s ☐ u l. She was not discouraged, however.

10. Instead, she ☐ r ☐ v e l ☐ e d to Crimea with her friend Thomas

     Day. There, they set up "The British Hotel", a place which provided warm rooms

11. for sick and ☐ n j u ☐ ☐ d soldiers.

12. In 2016, a statue was built in ☐ o n o ☐ r of Mary Seacole in London.

Underline the word that means the same, or nearly the same, as the word on the left.

Example: **fast**   <u>rapid</u>   slow   chase   fly

13. **wiggle**   jump   spin   squirm   chatter

14. **damaging**   harmful   disaster   demolish   poisonous

15. **pillar**   column   tower   roof   stone

16. **beg**   ask   desire   plead   give

17. **broadcast**   television   aerial   radio   transmit

Complete the word on the right so that it means the opposite, or nearly the opposite, of the word on the left.

Example: strong   [w][e][a][k]

18. powerful   [p][ ][ ][ ][y]

19. rural   [ ][r][b][ ][n]

20. noon   [m][i][ ][ ][i][ ][ ][t]

21. drop   [c][a][ ][ ][h]

22. departure [a][ ][ ][ ][i][ ][a][l]

The words on the left are related in some way.
Choose the word from the brackets that fits best with the words on the left.

Example: **car bus ferry coach** (road drive <u>train</u> cargo journey)

23. **giggle chortle snigger cackle** (cough smile cheeky hiccup chuckle)

24. **aim objective ambition target** (final end goal method assess)

25. **amble stroll saunter wander** (skip jump hop climb roam)

26. **wasp ant butterfly bee** (beetle snake crab insect mouse)

END OF TEST

/ 26

Test 5

You have **10 minutes** to do this test. Work as quickly and as accurately as you can.

Read this passage carefully and answer the questions that follow.

Mysterious Alice

It was an unusually warm day for April. Scanning the newspapers that morning, you'd have thought it was more than just a sunny spell. The panicked headlines warned of the dangers of being outside in the sunshine, but as I sat down at my usual lunch spot on the grassy hill, the temperature felt pleasant rather than
5 scorching. My thoughts turned, as they often did at that time, to the village's strange new resident.

Ever since Alice had arrived in the village, I'd known there was something unusual about her. She claimed she'd come to stay with her grandmother in the run-down mansion on the main road. I was suspicious. I was certain that no-one
10 had lived in the house for a long time. Its lawn had grown as high as my waist and its dense hedges spilt onto the pavement. Before Alice arrived, I swear I'd not seen anyone come in or out of the building for years.

My daydreaming was interrupted by the faint sound of rustling coming from the field at the bottom of the hill. A small patch of wheat began to move as if it had a
15 life of its own. The sun was incredibly bright and I had to squint to make out the source of the noise. As my eyes started to adjust to the brightness, I saw a wisp of golden hair duck suddenly below the top of the wheat. Who could it be?

I headed down the hill to investigate, but tripped on a small ledge and tumbled down into the field. Brushing the dirt off my trousers, I got up and pushed my way
20 through the crops. I'd lost track of whoever had been making the noise during my fall, but they'd left a tiny piece of pink plastic. I picked it up. It was unmistakably Alice's hair clip.

20

Answer these questions about the text that you've just read.
Circle the letter that matches the correct answer.

1. How does the narrator feel about the hot weather?

    A   Worried

    B   Exhausted

    C   Panicked

    D   Pleased

2. Why is the narrator suspicious of Alice?

    A   The narrator doesn't think anyone lives in the mansion with Alice.

    B   She is new to the village.

    C   She doesn't like the hot weather.

    D   Her hedges spill onto the pavement.

3. Why can't the narrator see the source of the rustling straight away?

    A   The rustling stops too quickly.

    B   Alice has run off.

    C   It is too far away.

    D   The sun is too bright.

4. Why does the narrator lose track of the person in the wheat?

    A   The sun is too bright.

    B   They can't see through the wheat.

    C   The narrator falls down the hill.

    D   Alice vanishes.

5. How does the narrator know it was Alice in the field?

   A   The narrator hears her voice.

   B   The narrator finds something belonging to Alice in the field.

   C   The narrator knows Alice likes to play in the wheat.

   D   The narrator recognises her hair.

6. What does "dense" (line 11) mean?

   A   Soft

   B   Tall

   C   Thick

   D   Prickly

7. What does "wisp" (line 16) mean?

   A   Strand

   B   Mess

   C   Chunk

   D   Head

The words on the left are related in some way. Choose the word from the brackets that fits best with the words on the left.

Example: **car bus ferry coach** (road   drive   <u>train</u>   cargo   journey)

---

8. **armchair stool sofa throne** (bench   table   cabinet   blanket   sitting)

9. **measles tonsillitis flu mumps** (fever   ill   injection   chickenpox   medicine)

10. **courageous plucky brave daring** (mighty   clever   fearless   scared   powerful)

11. **eagle owl hawk vulture** (fly   falcon   badger   bird   budgie)

12. **Jupiter Neptune Saturn Mars** (planet rocket Moon Sun Earth)

13. **trumpet bugle horn tuba** (trombone guitar instrument music drums)

14. **football hockey basketball cricket** (sport team climbing rugby swim)

> Underline the word that means the same,
> or nearly the same, as the word on the left.
>
> **Example:** **fast** <u>rapid</u> slow chase fly

15. **ridicule**   laugh   argue   mock   funny

16. **ache**   wound   soreness   suffer   cut

17. **stutter**   stammer   trip   stumble   speak

18. **gifted**   talented   lucky   spoilt   happy

19. **grab**   touch   clasp   feel   carry

20. **slope**   ski   slant   mountain   flat

END OF TEST

/ 20

Time for a break! This puzzle is a great way to practise your **word-making** skills.

Mystery Meeting

Steve the Spy has been given directions to a secret meeting, but some of the words have been written in code.

Half of each answer is written in the clue — the other half is the way the clue is presented. Write the completed words on the lines at the bottom of the page.

An example is shown to the right.

popcorn

Leave your house and go past the fields with   Hay Hay Hay
Hay Hay Hay
Hay Hay Hay . When you

reach the , turn left. Follow this road until you are level with a

 on your right. On your left will be a wall with a door.

Go through the door and into a garden. Go over to the . Twist

the metal part  WISE and a secret entrance will be revealed.

_____   _____   _____

_____   _____

You have **10 minutes** to do this test. Work as quickly and as accurately as you can.

Choose the correct words to complete the passage below.

1. ☐ cold
Iceland is a ☐ land   of extremes. Despite being such a cold place,
☐ places

2. ☐ number
Iceland has a large ☐ smoke   of active volcanoes. In 2010, a volcano
☐ eruptions

3. ☐ exploded
☐ lava   Eyjafjallajökull erupted, causing huge amounts of dust to be
☐ named

4. ☐ appeared
☐ released   into the air. There is a volcanic eruption once every four years on
☐ clouds

5. ☐ average   6. ☐ definitely
☐ volcano. While Iceland's name   ☐ don't   suggest that it's a cold place,
☐ exactly   ☐ might

7. ☐ extra
the heat produced by its volcanoes is used to create electricity. In   ☐ addition ,
☐ also

8. ☐ warmth
the high temperatures ☐ swim   pools of water, also known as thermal spas,
☐ heat

9.
which are very   ☐ common
  ☐ unknown   with tourists. There are also waterfalls, glaciers and
  ☐ popular

10.
mountains which give Iceland its   ☐ wide
  ☐ breathtaking   landscape. For a few months
  ☐ first

11.
during the summer, Iceland   ☐ enjoys
  ☐ enjoy   nearly continuous sunlight — that means it
  ☐ enjoying

12.
doesn't get   ☐ dark
  ☐ night   .
  ☐ midnight

Four of the words in each list are linked. Underline the word that is **not** related to the other four.

Example: cow   hen   sheep   pig   <u>monkey</u>

13. parsley   basil   onion   coriander   thyme

14. enthusiast   fan   follower   supporter   expert

15. nettle   poppy   pansy   rose   lily

16. helmet   hood   bonnet   sock   cap

17. myth   legend   book   fable   folklore

Complete the word on the right so that it means the same, or nearly the same, as the word on the left.

Example: foe   e n e m y

18. bog   m ☐ r ☐ h
19. beak   b ☐ l ☐
20. lucky   f o ☐ u ☐ a ☐ ☐
21. sociable   o u ☐ ☐ o i ☐ g

The words on the left are related in some way. Choose the word from the brackets that fits best with the words on the left.

Example: **car bus ferry coach** (road drive <u>train</u> cargo journey)

22. **kettle microwave dishwasher fridge** (teapot toaster TV kitchen radiator)

23. **stem leaf seed root** (tree bush sunflower petal plant)

24. **pout grimace smirk frown** (lips grin guffaw lick grunt)

25. **octopus oyster starfish shrimp** (seaweed jellyfish reef tropical rock)

26. **dune mountain mound peak** (valley river plain hill canyon)

END OF TEST

/ 26

You have **10 minutes** to do this test. Work as quickly and as accurately as you can.

Read this passage carefully and answer the questions that follow.

The King in the Car Park

Of all the places to find a king's grave, a car park in Leicester is surely one of
the most unusual, but that's exactly what happened in 2012. The grave belonged
to King Richard III, who ruled England during the 1400s. Richard was part of the
House of York, a powerful family whose symbol was the white rose.

5   His reign was troubled, however, and a rival family, the House of Lancaster,
believed that Richard shouldn't be king. He was eventually killed in 1485 during
a battle between the Houses of York and Lancaster. Richard was buried in a
friary* which was demolished in the mid-16th century, meaning that his body's
whereabouts have long been unknown.

10   In August 2012, a team began to search for the missing king. They tracked down
the location of the former friary, began excavating and eventually found a human
skeleton. Experts dated the bones back to the 15th century and its severely curved
spine fit some descriptions of Richard. However, just finding the bones was not
enough to be sure that they belonged to the king. Six months later, the University of

15 Leicester used DNA evidence to confirm that they were in fact Richard III's.

In 2015, a reburial was held in Leicester for the king. A grand procession took
place in the city centre, and the streets were lined with people carrying white roses
in honour of the king. The Queen sent a message to be read as the crowd entered
Leicester cathedral, where Richard was buried. Not everyone was pleased about

20 the burial, however. A group claiming to be descendants of Richard thought that
the king would have wanted to have been buried in York.

*friary — *a sort of monastery*

Answer these questions about the text that you've just read.
Circle the letter that matches the correct answer.

1. According to the text, which of the following must be true?

    A   The site of the friary where Richard was buried became a car park.

    B   Everyone was pleased that Richard was reburied in Leicester.

    C   Richard III was from the House of Lancaster.

    D   Richard III is the only monarch to have been to Leicester.

2. Why did the team dig up the car park?

    A   They wanted to find the graveyard of the old friary.

    B   They wanted to make improvements to the car park.

    C   The Queen demanded it.

    D   They thought the car park was haunted.

3. How long did it take to confirm that the bones were Richard's after they were discovered?

    A   One year

    B   Six months

    C   Six years

    D   One month

4. Why were the experts certain that the skeleton belonged to Richard?

    A   It was located in the car park.

    B   It had a curved spine like Richard.

    C   They knew he was buried in Leicester.

    D   They used DNA evidence.

5. Why did people watching the procession carry white roses?

    A   They are a traditional funeral flower.

    B   They were Richard's favourite flower.

    C   They were the symbol of Richard's family.

    D   Richard's body was found buried with one.

6. Why do you think the funeral was "grand" (line 16)?

    A   Because Richard was a king and deserved an impressive funeral.

    B   Because the team who found Richard wanted to celebrate their discovery.

    C   Because the descendants of Richard demanded it.

    D   Because the team wanted to make up for the fact he wasn't buried in York.

7. Why did some people think the king should have been buried in York?

    A   Because York is more popular with tourists.

    B   Leicester did not support the king.

    C   Richard belonged to the House of York.

    D   York has a nicer cathedral.

Rearrange the words so that each sentence makes sense.
Underline the word which doesn't fit into the sentence.

    Example: to I have <u>lamp</u> room my tidy

---

8. on bus felt Carla sick the van

9. two ice ate paid I for creams

10. brought picnic fork pies for the I pork

11. live the kangaroo forests in Australia of koalas

12. during he film snores asleep the fell

13. baked cook always her for scones Joanna friends

14. is speaks Chinese language learn hard to a

Underline the word below that means the opposite,
or nearly the opposite, of the word on the left.

Example: ill   nice   <u>well</u>   sick   happy

15. **spotless**   filthy   spotty   clean   stripy

16. **well-behaved**   evil   cheerful   upset   naughty

17. **splendid**   fabulous   magnificent   unimpressive   tired

18. **chilly**   icy   warm   passionate   unwelcoming

19. **drowsy**   sleepy   snooze   thirsty   alert

20. **part**   section   separate   everything   whole

END OF TEST

/ 20

31

Test 8

You have **10 minutes** to do this test. Work as quickly and as accurately as you can.

Choose the correct words to complete the passage below.

The Eden Project in Cornwall is made up of two huge bubble-like greenhouses

1. ☐ containing
   ☐ massive   with plants. Containing over 5,000
   ☐ filled

2. ☐ types
   ☐ parts   of plant, the
   ☐ leaves

Eden Project aims to teach children and adults about the natural

3. ☐ outside
   ☐ world   ,
   ☐ animals

as well as the importance of looking

4. ☐ before
   ☐ by   our planet. The project aims to be
   ☐ after

as energy efficient as

5. ☐ possible
   ☐ renewable. All of the plants are watered
   ☐ likely

6. ☐ using
   ☐ without
   ☐ across

recycled rainwater. Inside the first greenhouse is the largest indoor rainforest in the

7. ☐ Britain
   ☐ Cornwall. The tropical temperatures allow a
   ☐ world

8. ☐ range
   ☐ every   of plants from
   ☐ many

32

Malaysia, South America and West Africa to grow, while the second greenhouse creates

a warm, dry environment
9. ☐ alike
☐ similar   to the climate of the Mediterranean.
☐ copying

At the Eden Project, you can
10. ☐ learn
☐ educated how coffee, bananas and bamboo
☐ reading

11. ☐ grown
are   ☐ grew   . There are also some outdoor gardens which feature a wide array of
☐ ate

12. ☐ native
plants   ☐ natural   to Cornwall, as well as other milder regions.
☐ wild

> Rearrange the words so that each sentence makes sense.
> Underline the word which doesn't fit into the sentence.
>
> **Example**:   to I have <u>lamp</u> room my tidy

13. chattering the teeth his were cold was from

14. respond my ask didn't Rishi message to

15. about brag the competition winning was gloating Gordon

16. dogs always was Jack Russell the yapping

33   Test 9

17. **hurricane cyclone typhoon blizzard** (tornado wet windy warm rain)

18. **hammock bed bunk cot** (couch bedroom crib quilt blanket)

19. **magpie raven robin starling** (ostrich pelican crow fox penguin)

20. **rotten sour decaying stale** (smelly mouldy nasty hard flavourless)

21. **rubbish garbage litter trash** (dust dirty bin treasure junk)

22. infrequent ⟨c⟩⟨o⟩⟨ ⟩⟨s⟩⟨ ⟩⟨a⟩⟨ ⟩⟨t⟩

23. airy ⟨s⟩⟨t⟩⟨ ⟩⟨f⟩⟨ ⟩⟨ ⟩

24. compulsory ⟨ ⟩⟨ ⟩⟨l⟩⟨u⟩⟨n⟩⟨t⟩⟨ ⟩⟨ ⟩⟨y⟩

25. end ⟨ ⟩⟨e⟩⟨g⟩⟨i⟩⟨ ⟩⟨n⟩⟨ ⟩⟨n⟩⟨ ⟩

26. insult ⟨c⟩⟨ ⟩⟨m⟩⟨p⟩⟨ ⟩⟨ ⟩⟨m⟩⟨e⟩⟨ ⟩⟨ ⟩

END OF TEST

/ 26

Time for a break! This puzzle is a great way to practise your **vocabulary** skills.

Chocolate Challenge

Pete's mum has organised a chocolate treasure hunt in the garden for Pete and his friends. She has written clues to the location of the chocolate, and the answer to each one is a word to do with treasure.
Write the answer to each clue on the lines. Then unscramble the letters in the blue boxes to reveal the location of the chocolate.

Unscramble these letters to find me:
l i v e r s

☐ __ __ __ __ __

Unscramble these letters to find me: **f u t e r o n**

__ __ __ __ ☐ __ __

I am the opposite of 'worthless'.
__ a __ ☐ __ __ __ __

I rhyme with 'health'.
__ __ __ ☐ __ __

Complete the sentence below.
The pirate's chest was full of golden
☐ __ o __ i __ s .

Unscramble these letters to find me:
e i s u p r c o

__ __ __ __ __ ☐ __ __

I am buried underneath the _____ .

You have **10 minutes** to do this test. Work as quickly and as accurately as you can.

Fill in the missing letters to complete the words in the following passage.

1. Just [o][ ][t][s][ ][ ][e] the northern city of Bradford lies Saltaire, a

2. village named after a Victorian business [ ][w][n][ ][ ] called Titus

    Salt. He built the massive Salt's Mill here for manufacturing textiles. Salt

3. wanted to provide his [w][ ][r][k][ ][ ][s] with a good standard of living, so

4. he built them high-quality housing [ ][l][o][s][ ] to their place of work, a

5. [h][ ][s][p][ ][ ][a][l] and even churches. This was very unusual at the

6. time [ ][e][c][a][ ][s][ ] many people who worked in factories lived in

7. [p][ ][v][e][ ][t][y]. Disease was widespread and many people in Bradford

8. did not [s][u][ ][v][ ][v][e] into adulthood.

9. Salt's Mill [c][ ][n][t][ ][ ][u][e][ ] making textiles until 1986, and the

10. village was made a UNESCO World Heritage Site in 2001. [ ][o][d][a][ ],

11. the village is a popular tourist [ ][t][t][r][ ][c][t][ ][ ][n] and the mill

12. is now home to an art [g][ ][ ][l][ ][e][r][ ] and a variety of shops.

Four of the words in each list are linked. Underline the word that is **not** related to the other four.

Example: cow   hen   sheep   pig   <u>monkey</u>

13. cod   salmon   haddock   tuna   crab

14. stain   blemish   dusty   blotch   smudge

15. muffin   doughnut   cake   sandwich   cookie

16. puddle   dirt   soil   earth   mud

17. pummel   whack   smack   punch   crash

Complete the word on the right so that it means the same, or nearly the same, as the word on the left.

Example: foe   [e][n][e][m][y]

18. calm   [t][ ][a][ ][q][u][i][ ]

19. eternal   [f][o][ ][ ][v][e][ ]

20. swap   [c][ ][a][ ][g][e]

21. cove   [b][ ][ ]

22. climb   [ ][s][c][e][ ][d]

Rearrange the words so that each sentence makes sense. Underline the word which doesn't fit into the sentence.

Example: to I have <u>lamp</u> room my tidy

23. worried my canoe sank I capsize was would

24. very blows outside there were strong winds

25. Tony spilt on floor coffee himself hot

26. anything all quiet Laura said morning hardly

END OF TEST

/ 26

10

You have **10 minutes** to do this test. Work as quickly and as accurately as you can.

Read this passage carefully and answer the questions that follow.

An adapted extract from 'The Mystery of the Semi-Detached'

The policeman barely acknowledged him as he passed. The cyclists went by him like grey ghosts. It was nearly ten o'clock and she had not come.

He shrugged his shoulders and turned towards his house. His road led him by her house and he walked slowly as he neared it. She might, even now, be coming out.
5 But she was not. There was no sign of movement about the house, no sign of life, no lights illuminating the windows.

He paused by the gate, wondering.

Then he noticed that the front door was open — wide open — and the street lamp shone a little way into the dark hall. There was something about all this that did not
10 please him — that scared him a little. The house had a gloomy and deserted air.

He walked up the path and listened. No sign of life. He passed into the hall. There was no light anywhere. Where was everybody, and why was the front door open? There was no one in the living-room — the dining-room and the study were equally empty. Everyone was out, evidently. But the unpleasant feeling that he
15 was, perhaps, not the first visitor to walk through that open door forced him to look through the house. So he went upstairs, and at the door of the first bedroom he came to he struck a match, as he had done in the living-room. Even as he did so he felt that he was not alone.

E. Nesbit

Answer these questions about the text that you've just read.
Circle the letter that matches the correct answer.

1. Line 2 refers to the cyclists as "grey ghosts". This suggests:

   A   they are scary.

   B   they are cycling through a graveyard.

   C   they are difficult to see.

   D   they aren't looking where they are going.

2. How does the narrator feel when the woman he was waiting for doesn't show up?

   A   He isn't that bothered.

   B   He is really worried.

   C   He is tired.

   D   He is quite pleased.

3. Why did the narrator go to the woman's house?

   A   He wanted to see where she lived.

   B   It was on his way home.

   C   He wanted to confront her about not turning up.

   D   He wanted a longer walk.

4. Why does the narrator decide to look around the house?

   A   Because he could hear the woman's voice

   B   To see how big the house was

   C   Because a window had been left open upstairs

   D   Because he thought it was strange that the door was open

5. How does the narrator feel when he goes into the house?

   A   Excited

   B   Disgusted

   C   Uncomfortable

   D   Confident

6. What does "gloomy" (line 10) mean?

   A   Dirty

   B   Upset

   C   Dark

   D   Bright

7. What does "unpleasant" (line 14) mean?

   A   Horrible

   B   Unfriendly

   C   Awkward

   D   Shocking

Complete the word on the right so that it means the opposite, or nearly the opposite, of the word on the left.

Example: strong   w e a k

8. truthful   d _ s _ o n e _ t

9. generous   s t _ _ g _

10. multiply   d i _ i _ e

11. fail   s   c   e   e

12. unfunny   i   l   r   i   o   s

13. repel   t   t   a   t

14. easy   c h   l   l   n   i n

Four of the words in each list are linked. Underline the word that is **not** related to the other four.

Example: cow   hen   sheep   pig   <u>monkey</u>

---

15. leaflet   newspaper   magazine   writing   brochure

16. cube   pyramid   rectangle   cylinder   sphere

17. archery   karate   judo   boxing   wrestling

18. grumble   moan   complain   whinge   sob

19. fence   railing   wall   hedge   gate

20. stir   snip   chop   slice   carve

END OF TEST

/ 20

Time for a break! This puzzle is a great way to practise your **logic** skills.

Finding Friends

Juliet and her friends are playing a game. Each of her friends has hidden in a different place in her garden. Their hiding places are marked by the numbers below. Each person has given Juliet a clue to where they are hiding.

Use the clues to work out who is hiding where.
For each person, write the correct number in the box below.

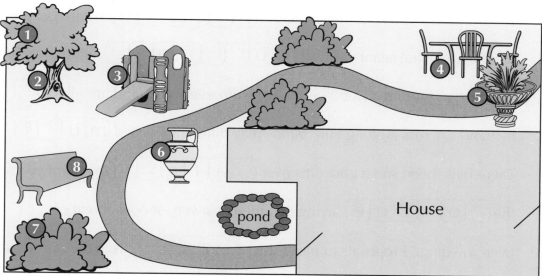

Max: "I am higher up than everyone else."

George: "I am directly below Max."

Tasha: "I am sitting down next to the path."

Neil: "I am hiding next to Max and George."

Claire: "I am the furthest away from Rita."

Priya: "I am closest to the pond."

Fred: "I am closest to the house."

Rita: "I can't see the pond."

(10)

You have **10 minutes** to do this test. Work as quickly and as accurately as you can.

Fill in the missing letters to complete the words in the following passage.

1. Notting Hill Carnival takes ☐l a☐☐ every August in London and is the

2. largest street festival in Europe. The carnival has been held every y☐a☐

3. since 1966 and a i☐☐ to celebrate Caribbean culture.

4. Thousands of visitors come to see the p☐r a☐e, where people

5. dress up in extravagant carnival c o☐☐☐m e☐ and dance through

6. the streets. Around 15,000 outfits are worn every year and are all m☐☐e

7. by hand. Across Notting Hill, bands play different types of m u☐i☐.

8. There have been some concerns over ☐a f e☐☐y in recent years, with

9. the ☐o☐i c e saying that there is a very serious threat of

10. overcrowding. Proposals to move the e v☐n☐ from the narrow streets

11. of Notting Hill to the far more s☐a c☐☐u s Hyde Park have,

12. however, been rejected. Similar carnivals are also held in ☐t h☐☐

cities, such as Bristol and Leeds.

The words on the left are related in some way. Choose the word from the brackets that fits best with the words on the left.

Example: **car bus ferry coach** (road drive <u>train</u> cargo journey)

13. **maths history science English** (subject assembly break lesson art)

14. **smash crush trample scrunch** (broken stand squash fold bang)

15. **brook river creek canal** (lake sea stream water pond)

16. **hungry cold sweaty thirsty** (annoyed thrilled sleepy upset sarcastic)

17. **pine sycamore willow birch** (tree oak rose acorn forest)

Rearrange the words so that each sentence makes sense. Underline the word which doesn't fit into the sentence.

Example: to I have <u>lamp</u> room my tidy

18. in cold was it stayed so fire I

19. tigers make good don't pets very fiercely

20. trod I puddle in fallen muddy a

21. went for we picnic a sandwiches yesterday

22. sofa sat inside George video playing games

Underline the word below that means the opposite, or nearly the opposite, of the word on the left.

Example: ill   nice   <u>well</u>   sick   happy

23. **outstanding**   unusual   perfect   ordinary   complicated

24. **fake**   forged   real   trusting   clever

25. **comical**   funny   deadly   serious   hilarious

26. **blocked**   squared   clear   stuck   busy

END OF TEST

/ 26

You have **10 minutes** to do this test. Work as quickly and as accurately as you can.

Read this passage carefully and answer the questions that follow.

Krampus

I'm sure the last thing to come to mind when you think of Christmas is a goat-like demon who kidnaps naughty children. However, in Austria and Southern Germany, a monster called the Krampus is a spooky addition to the otherwise cosy Christmas period.

5   The Krampus is a hairy, huge-horned monster with hooved feet and fangs. He loudly rattles chains, bells and birch twigs and has a basket strapped to his back to steal any children who have misbehaved. Legend has it that on 5th December, the Krampus visits the houses of those children who have disobeyed their parents during the previous year. This is called Krampus night. In certain parts of Austria,

10   parents attach birch twigs to the outside of their houses throughout the year to remind their children what will happen if they are not good.

Stories of the Krampus go back to ancient times in Austria, and this fearsome creature has become a popular part of Austrian celebrations in the run-up to Christmas. Originating around 400 years ago, 'Krampus runs' take place in many

15   Austrian towns, where people dress up in Krampus costumes, march through the streets, noisily ring bells and frighten onlookers. Children come to the town centre to watch the parade and see if they are brave enough to face the Krampus.

If you thought you were safe by not living in Austria, think again! Thanks to the internet, the Krampus has already taken the American media by storm and some

20   American cities have even hosted their own Krampus runs. Let's hope this terrifying tradition doesn't make it to the UK!

Answer these questions about the text that you've just read.
Circle the letter that matches the correct answer.

1. According to the text, which of the following does the Krampus not carry?

   A   Sweets

   B   Sticks

   C   Bells

   D   A basket

2. Which of the following facts is given in the text?

   A   How many houses the Krampus visits

   B   Which town has the most famous Krampus run

   C   Who invented the Krampus legend

   D   The date of Krampus night

3. Which of the following statements is false?

   A   The Krampus is said to have hooves.

   B   The Krampus is said to visit on Christmas Eve.

   C   Some parents in Austria attach birch twigs to their houses on Krampus night.

   D   The Krampus is said to kidnap naughty children.

4. When did the "Krampus run" tradition begin?

   A   The 1600s

   B   In ancient times

   C   The 1800s

   D   Around 10 years ago

5. Which of the following words could not be used to describe the Krampus?

   A   Hairy

   B   Quiet

   C   Unfriendly

   D   Frightening

6. What reason does the text give for Krampus traditions spreading across the world?

   A   Tourists are bringing it back from Austria.

   B   Austrians living in the rest of the world are spreading the legend.

   C   People have learnt about Krampus traditions from the internet.

   D   The Krampus also existed in American legends.

7. According to the passage, which of the following statements must be true?

   A   The Krampus has now become popular in the UK.

   B   The Krampus is now more popular in America than in Austria.

   C   The Krampus is becoming more and more popular in America.

   D   The internet has made Krampus night more popular in Austria.

Rearrange the words so that each sentence makes sense.
Underline the word which doesn't fit into the sentence.

Example: to I have <u>lamp</u> room my tidy

---

8. are to plane flying on Dublin Saturday we

9. school at play badminton on shuttlecock Tuesdays I

10. sneakily all François the gobbling biscuits ate

11. curly talked sister my hair has brown

12. tomorrow   nine   arrive   trip   please   o'clock   at

13. read   all   books   shelf   Sally   of   has   her

14. buying   cream   quickly   cakes   are   selling   the

Complete the word on the right so that it means the same, or nearly the same, as the word on the left.

Example: foe   [e][n][e][m][y]

15. injury   [w][ ][u][n][ ]

16. shout   [y][ ][l][ ]

17. youth   [c][h][ ][ ][d][ ][o][o][d]

18. faithful   [ ][o][y][ ][l]

19. lazy   [ ][d][l][ ]

20. sturdy   [t][ ][ ][g][h]

END OF TEST

/ 20

You have **10 minutes** to do this test. Work as quickly and as accurately as you can.

Read this passage carefully and answer the questions that follow.

Ghosts in the Tower

Have you ever had the feeling that someone, or something, was watching you even when you were alone? Or have you ever heard strange noises that can't be explained? What about feeling a room go suddenly very cold? These are just some of the strange sensations that are often experienced by people who are thought to
5   have encountered a ghost.

Ghosts are often associated with old buildings, especially those that have had a grisly past. One such building is the Tower of London — a former royal residence that was used as a prison for many years. In its 900-year history, the Tower of London has seen approximately 100 executions, many of which were beheadings.
10   One of the most famous beheadings was that of Anne Boleyn (the second wife of King Henry VIII) who was executed in 1536. Anne's ghost is supposed to haunt the site of her execution, and several people have witnessed a ghostly figure carrying a head under its arm.

Another phantom that supposedly haunts the Tower of London is the ghost of Lady
15 Jane Grey. Lady Jane was put on the throne by meddling nobles, but her cousin, Mary, had other ideas, and ordered her execution. Jane's ghost has been seen wandering the battlements of the Tower — often around the anniversary of her death.

Perhaps the most surprising ghost that is said to haunt the Tower of London is the ghost of a bear. The Tower of London has been home to numerous exotic animals
20 over the years, often gifts from foreign royals, and two bears once resided at the Tower. Sightings of the ghostly bear are few and far between, but legend has it that a phantom bear once scared a Tower guard so badly that he dropped dead from shock!

Answer these questions about the text that you've just read.
Circle the letter that matches the correct answer.

1. Which of the following isn't mentioned in the text as a sign that a ghost is present?

    A   The feeling of being watched

    B   Unexplained noises

    C   Doors opening by themselves

    D   A drop in the room's temperature

2. According to the text, why is it unsurprising that the Tower of London is supposedly haunted?

    A   It's an old building with a gruesome past.

    B   Kings and queens often become ghosts after their deaths.

    C   London is the most haunted city in the world.

    D   Only people that are beheaded become ghosts.

3. Whose ghost apparently appears around the anniversary of their death?

    A   Anne Boleyn

    B   Lady Jane Grey

    C   Mary

    D   Henry VIII

4. According to the text, why could "exotic animals" (line 19) be found at the Tower of London?

    A   They were used to scare away ghosts.

    B   They were used to frighten the guards.

    C   They were presents from kings and queens from other countries.

    D   They were used to guard prisoners.

5. Which of the following best describes sightings of the ghostly bear?

   A   Rare and deadly

   B   Frequent and terrifying

   C   Funny and scary

   D   Rare and funny

6. What does "meddling" (line 15) mean?

   A   Interfering

   B   Repairing

   C   Loyal

   D   Evil

7. What does "resided" (line 20) mean?

   A   Died

   B   Lived

   C   Imprisoned

   D   Displayed

Find the word that means the same, or nearly the same, as the word on the left.

Example: **wide**   flat   straight   <u>broad</u>   long

8. **nearly**   far   distant   barely   almost

9. **mutter**   complain   chat   mumble   rumble

10. **spin**   wriggle   twirl   swing   wave

11. **blunder**   skill   insult   mistake   hurdle

       Test 14

12. **similar**   alike   different   unique   identical

13. **mild**   minor   strong   unhappy   mellow

14. **applaud**   cheer   clap   shout   encourage

Four of the words in each list are linked. Underline the word that is **not** related to the other four.

Example: cow   hen   sheep   pig   <u>monkey</u>

15. Arabic   Turkish   Japan   Korean   Chinese

16. pork   beef   chicken   sausage   turkey

17. repair   fix   mend   create   rebuild

18. turnip   sweetcorn   carrot   swede   parsnip

19. learner   apprentice   novice   manager   trainee

20. wheat   corn   barley   seeds   rye

END OF TEST

/ 20

Time for a break! This puzzle is a great way to practise your **word-making** skills.

Dragon Riddles

Neil the Knight has a dragon to slay. He has to pass through a series of doors and answer a riddle at each one to get to the dragon. Each answer is a letter and these letters can be rearranged to form a word which will reveal the dragon's secret weakness. Write each letter and the final unscrambled word on the lines.

My secret weakness is:
_____

If you add me to 'rode', you will find a word which means 'wearing away'. ____

If you remove me from 'cheat', you will find a word which means 'talk'. ____

Double me and add me to 'hi' and you will find a noise that snakes make. ____

If you add me to 'math', you will find something that lights fires. ____

If you remove me from 'shock', you will find an item of clothing. ____

Add me to the start and end of 'lit' and you will find a word which means 'superior'. ____

You have **10 minutes** to do this test. Work as quickly and as accurately as you can.

Choose the correct words to complete the passage below.

1. ☐ lit
In 1782, while   ☐ watching   the fireplace at his home in France, a man called
☐ waiting

2. ☐ wanted
Joseph-Michel Montgolfier   ☐ need   to understand what made smoke and
☐ likes

3. ☐ rising   4. ☐ fires
embers   ☐ rise   . He did some   ☐ examine   and found that a silk bag
☐ raise   ☐ experiments

5. ☐ filled
with a hole in the bottom floated in the air when   ☐ empty   with smoke. He
☐ make

6. ☐ heat
believed that the smoke   ☐ melted   a new gas, which he called Montgolfier gas.
☐ created

7. ☐ instead
Nowadays, we know that it's just hot air,   ☐ even   than smoke, that causes things
☐ rather

to float. Together with his brother Jacques-Étienne, Joseph created a hot-air balloon to

8. ☐ invent
   ☐ test   their discovery. The first
   ☐ think

9. ☐ airborne
   ☐ passengers   on a hot-air balloon were
   ☐ people

a duck, a cockerel and a sheep. The flight took place in

10. ☐ courtyard
    ☐ middle   of the royal
    ☐ front

palace in Versailles, where the King and Queen of France were in the

11. ☐ audience
    ☐ back   .
    ☐ throne

In 1783, the first manned flight of a hot air balloon travelled

12. ☐ definitely
    ☐ far   5.5 miles
    ☐ about

over Paris in 25 minutes.

Rearrange the words so that each sentence makes sense.
Underline the word which doesn't fit into the sentence.

Example: to I have <u>lamp</u> room my tidy

13. my   shorts   a   me   bought   new   mum   jumper

14. snake   into   bush   a   the   slide   slithered

15. concentrate   on   I   couldn't   my   focused   homework

16. his   the   in   with   threw   Will   trainers   bin

Underline the word below that means the opposite, or nearly the opposite, of the word on the left.

Example: **ill**   nice   <u>well</u>   sick   happy

17. **long-winded**   far   quiet   small   brief

18. **glum**   cheerful   sorry   miserable   brilliant

19. **nearby**   close   faraway   long   isolated

20. **wise**   foolish   intelligent   nonsense   understanding

21. **tender**   gentle   smooth   tough   jagged

Four of the words in each list are linked. Underline the word that is **not** related to the other four.

Example: cow   hen   sheep   pig   <u>monkey</u>

22. rake   spade   spoon   shears   hoe

23. shine   gold   glisten   sparkle   glimmer

24. reflect   think   contemplate   forget   ponder

25. aisle   corridor   bridge   passageway   alley

26. desk   mouse   keyboard   screen   scanner

END OF TEST

/ 26

You have **10 minutes** to do this test. Work as quickly and as accurately as you can.

Read this passage carefully and answer the questions that follow.

Uncle Charlie

The journey had felt endless. It was the first time Alex had left his hometown, let alone travelled to this remote part of the Scottish Highlands. He was sitting bolt upright in the backseat, clutching onto the handle of the car door. As his destination got nearer and nearer, his surroundings became more and more bleak, and he

5 became more and more worried. There were no houses, shops or people on the streets, only the odd telephone wire along the edge of the forest. It was 3 o'clock in the afternoon, but it felt as if it were the middle of the night. The sun was covered by a thick layer of grey clouds, though there was not a drop of rain.

The car took a sharp left, struggling up a steep country lane, before pulling up to a

10 run-down old farmhouse. Alex's heart sank when he saw his new home. Before he had chance to beg the driver to take him back, he was interrupted by an enormous commotion. At that moment, a round little man burst suddenly through the front door of the farmhouse, almost falling face-first onto the gravel driveway, before catching himself at the last moment. Tufts of bright white hair sprouted from behind

15 his ears and a curled white moustache covered his violet cheeks. His clothes were old-fashioned and expensive-looking, but his movements were awkward. After quickly wiping his hands on his trousers, he presented Alex with his hand to shake and rattled it frantically.

"Ahh, you must be Alex," he said, in a jolly, nasal voice.

20 Alex let out an immediate sigh of relief. He began to introduce himself to his host, but it seemed Uncle Charlie had already got distracted. "I really must show you… Now where have I put the thingamajig?"

Answer these questions about the text that you've just read.
Circle the letter that matches the correct answer.

1. How is Alex feeling when he is in the car?

    A   Excited

    B   Silly

    C   Nervous

    D   Thoughtful

2. In line 10, Alex's "heart sank". This means:

    A   he has suddenly fallen in love.

    B   he feels suddenly disappointed and worried.

    C   he has medical problems with his heart.

    D   he feels suddenly jealous.

3. Which of the following statements must be true?

    A   Alex has lived with Uncle Charlie for many years.

    B   Alex was forced to leave his old home.

    C   Uncle Charlie is very rich.

    D   Uncle Charlie lives in the Scottish Highlands.

4. Why does Alex feel relieved in line 20?

    A   Uncle Charlie doesn't fall over.

    B   Uncle Charlie is easily distracted.

    C   He is going home.

    D   Uncle Charlie seems friendly.

5. Which word best describes Uncle Charlie?

   A   Clumsy

   B   Serious

   C   Bad-tempered

   D   Sophisticated

6. What does "bleak" (line 4) mean?

   A   Busy

   B   Cloudy

   C   Dreary

   D   Quiet

7. What does "commotion" (line 12) mean?

   A   Mess

   B   Accident

   C   Thunderstorm

   D   Uproar

The words on the left are related in some way. Choose the word from the brackets that fits best with the words on the left.

   Example: **car bus ferry coach** (road drive <u>train</u> cargo journey)

---

8. **gerbil mouse chipmunk rat** (badger hamster rodent mammal deer)

9. **batch bunch clump lot** (cluster individual large many arrange)

10. **wizard conjurer sorcerer magician** (wand magic ogre witch toad)

11. **pillow mattress cushion sheet** (bed sofa soft pyjamas duvet)

12. **cabin den shed shack** (house hut flat room dwelling)

13. **sliver fragment snippet smidge** (chunk amount morsel lump dollop)

14. **roundabout swing slide sandpit** (park seesaw playground play ball)

Rearrange the words so that each sentence makes sense.
Underline the word which doesn't fit into the sentence.

Example: to I have <u>lamp</u> room my tidy

---

15. speak learning can she different languages three

16. is Josh eggs at Easter visit to coming

17. for the rollercoaster long queue quickly the was

18. run in corridor you forbidden shouldn't the

19. laces tripped and fallen were Leanne's untied she

20. were the eaten chickens coop by fox a

END OF TEST

/ 20

This puzzle is a great way to practise your **logic** and **vocabulary** skills.

Friend or Foe?

Simon the Space Traveller can work out if a planet is friendly or hostile by decoding the signal it gives off. Use the clue to crack the code and write each letter in the boxes.

A B C D E F G H I J K L M N O P Q R S T U V W X Y Z

In the code, 'CLUE' becomes 'AJSC'

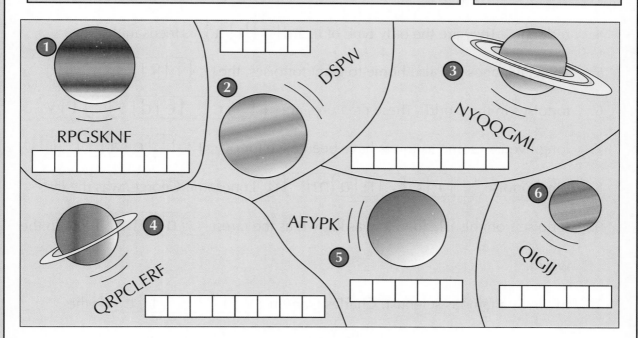

1 RPGSKNF

2 DSPW

3 NYQQGML

4 QRPCLERF

5 AFYPK

6 QIGJJ

Each word on Simon's computer is a synonym for each decoded word above. Find out which planets are friendly by writing the number of each planet in the box next to the correct synonym.

Friendly
Appeal ☐
Flair ☐
Success ☐

Hostile
Wrath ☐
Power ☐
Intensity ☐

(10)

You have **10 minutes** to do this test. Work as quickly and as accurately as you can.

Fill in the missing letters to complete the words in the following passage.

1.   The Galápagos are a [g][r][ ][u][ ] of islands in the Pacific Ocean. The

2.   islands are [ ][a][m][ ][u][s] for the unique species of animals that live

3.   there. Marine iguanas are one of the Galápagos's [s][t][r][ ][ ][e]

4.   residents. They are the only type of lizard [ ][h][a][ ] feeds in the sea.

5.   The Galápagos are also home to giant tortoises, the [ ][i][g][g][ ][ ][t]

6.   tortoises in the world. These creatures are [i][ ][c][ ][e][d][ ][l][y]

7.   long-lived — some tortoises have been alive for over 170 [ ][e][a][ ][ ].

8.   One tortoise, [ ][i][c][ ][n][a][m][ ][d] Lonesome George, was the last

9.   tortoise from his island. He was known as the rarest [ ][n][ ][m][a][ ] in the

       world.

10.   In 1835, a famous scientist, Charles Darwin, [v][i][ ][ ][t][e][d] the

11.   islands. He was [f][ ][s][c][ ][n][ ][t][e][d] by the different species

12.   that lived there. He wrote [a][ ][o][ ][t] a group of bird species, which are

       today known as 'Darwin's finches'.

Four of the words in each list are linked. Underline the word that is **not** related to the other four.

Example: cow   hen   sheep   pig   <u>monkey</u>

13. fry   boil   burn   poach   roast

14. village   county   town   city   hamlet

15. church   chapel   bible   cathedral   abbey

16. tent   pitch   caravan   campervan   motorhome

17. avenue   street   boulevard   lane   railway

Find the word that means the same, or nearly the same, as the word on the left.

Example: **wide**   flat   straight   <u>broad</u>   long

18. **frown**   huff   smile   scowl   gloom

19. **hike**   parade   hill   boot   trek

20. **hire**   utilise   employ   sack   fire

21. **important**   incredible   superior   amazing   significant

22. **specific**   particular   important   detailed   vague

The words on the left are related in some way. Choose the word from the brackets that fits best with the words on the left.

Example: **car bus ferry coach** (road drive <u>train</u> cargo journey)

23. **alligator crocodile turtle tortoise** (frog lizard reptile bite scale)

24. **bonnet boot engine accelerator** (drive car tyre speed race)

25. **linger loiter delay lag** (dawdle hurry slowly hesitating stranger)

26. **scissors pencil ruler rubber** (case desk pen book computer)

END OF TEST

/ 26

66

You have **10 minutes** to do this test. Work as quickly and as accurately as you can.

Read this passage carefully and answer the questions that follow.

Cryptids

'Cryptid' is a word used to describe an animal that is thought to be mythical, like the Loch Ness Monster or the yeti. However, there are a few cases where supposed cryptids have turned out to be real.

Towards the end of the nineteenth century, Western scientists thought that they
5   had discovered all the large animals in the world — but they were wrong! In 1890, an explorer called Sir Henry Morton Stanley reported that, during his travels in Africa, local people had spoken to him about 'a mysterious forest donkey' with black and white stripes on its back legs. Another explorer, Sir Harry Johnston, became fascinated with Stanley's stories of this secretive creature. Eleven years after Stanley's
10   report, Johnston found a skin belonging to the animal and sent it back to London, where scientists announced the discovery of a new type of zebra. Many people weren't sure whether the animal was real and called the animal an 'African unicorn'. Johnston later found a skull and confirmed from its shape that the animal was in fact a relative of the giraffe. It became known as the okapi and began to appear in
15   Western zoos soon after.

The okapi is not the only creature that was once thought to be made-up. For centuries, sailors have told stories of a gigantic squid-like creature capable of destroying ships — the kraken. It is thought that these stories stem from the rare occasions when dead giant squid, which live in the extreme depths of the ocean,
20   have washed up on shore. It was not until 2004 that Japanese scientists were able to photograph a giant squid living in the wild. The species remains mysterious to this day and much of what we know comes from dead squid found in the stomachs of whales.

Answer these questions about the text that you've just read.
Circle the letter that matches the correct answer.

1. Why do you think people originally thought the okapi was a "new type of zebra" (line 11)?

   A   It had a similar skull.

   B   It lived in Africa.

   C   It lived in forests.

   D   It had black and white stripes on its hind legs.

2. Which of the following statements about Sir Harry Johnston is true?

   A   He discovered the okapi in 1890.

   B   He thought the okapi was a kind of unicorn.

   C   He was inspired to search for the okapi by Sir Henry Morton Stanley.

   D   He thought that zebras were cryptids.

3. In which year did scientists in London wrongly announce the discovery of a new kind of zebra?

   A   1905

   B   1901

   C   1882

   D   1890

4. Why did people call the okapi an "African unicorn" (line 12)?

   A   They thought it was a 'cryptid', like a unicorn.

   B   It had one long horn.

   C   The skin Johnston found looked like a unicorn's.

   D   People thought it was magical, like a unicorn.

5. Why do you think we know so little about giant squid?

    A   They are dangerous and shouldn't be approached.

    B   Most of them have been eaten by whales.

    C   They live in the depths of the ocean so are rarely seen.

    D   They don't actually exist.

6. According to the text, which of the following best describes the kraken?

    A   A large creature that looks like a squid.

    B   A large creature that looks like a whale.

    C   A close relation of the Loch Ness Monster.

    D   No-one knows what it looks like.

7. Which of the following is an example of a cryptid?

    A   Giraffe

    B   Yeti

    C   Whale

    D   Giant squid

> Four of the words in each list are linked. Underline the word that is **not** related to the other four.
>
>   **Example**: cow hen sheep pig <u>monkey</u>

8. winter   seasons   summer   spring   autumn

9. badminton   darts   tennis   squash   ping-pong

10. harp   violin   drum   guitar   cello

11. wolf   jaguar   lion   tiger   cheetah

12. frank   honest   truthful   sincere   positive

13. squash   lemonade   cola   soup   juice

Find the word that means the same, or nearly the same, as the word on the left.

Example: **wide**   flat   straight   <u>broad</u>   long

14. **apartment**   home   terrace   flat   house

15. **thread**   string   pin   needle   knit

16. **awkward**   crude   trip   graceful   graceless

17. **clutter**   tidy   strewn   mess   dirt

18. **blossom**   bud   fruit   bloom   shrivel

19. **rage**   cry   pleasure   irritate   fury

20. **desire**   entertain   please   crave   idea

END OF TEST

/ 20

You have **10 minutes** to do this test. Work as quickly and as accurately as you can.

Fill in the missing letters to complete the words in the following passage.

1. One year after the Great Plague of 1665, ☐n☐o☐h☐e☐☐ disaster struck

2. London. A small a☐c☐☐d☐e☐n☐☐☐l fire in a bakery on Pudding

3. Lane began the Great Fire of London. At that t☐i☐☐☐, buildings in

4. London were ☐o☐s☐☐l☐y made from wood and were tightly packed

5. t☐o☐☐e☐t☐☐☐r. This allowed the fire to spread incredibly

6. ☐u☐i☐☐k☐l☐. There was no organised fire brigade and people were

7. ☐n☐s☐u☐r☐ how best to stop the fire. St. Paul's Cathedral was one of

8. the buildings d☐e☐s☐☐o☐y☐☐d by the fire. According to the

9. official figures, only six people died, t☐☐o☐☐g☐h many believe that

10. the death toll must have been much ☐☐i☐g☐h☐☐r. Sir Christopher Wren

11. was given the t☐☐☐☐k of rebuilding the cathedral, as well as 51 other

12. churches ☐c☐r☐☐s☐☐ the city.

Rearrange the words so that each sentence makes sense.
Underline the word which doesn't fit into the sentence.

Example: to I have <u>lamp</u> room my tidy

13. request sandwiches three asked he for me

14. to children have I look care the after

15. am theatre tonight play seeing I a

16. a at nurse paramedics Sean is the hospital

17. around night the fire we sat all dark

Complete the word on the right so that it means the same,
or nearly the same, as the word on the left.

Example: foe ⟨e⟩⟨n⟩⟨e⟩⟨m⟩⟨y⟩

18. speedy ⟨p⟩⟨r⟩⟨ ⟩⟨ ⟩⟨ ⟩⟨t⟩

19. horrid ⟨f⟩⟨o⟩⟨ ⟩⟨l⟩

20. acquire ⟨o⟩⟨ ⟩⟨ ⟩⟨a⟩⟨i⟩⟨n⟩

21. zone ⟨a⟩⟨ ⟩⟨e⟩⟨ ⟩

22. cab ⟨ ⟩⟨a⟩⟨x⟩⟨ ⟩

72

Underline the word below that means the opposite, or nearly the opposite, of the word on the left.

Example: **ill**   nice <u>well</u> sick happy

23. **sorrow**   happy joyous misery glee

24. **grumpy**   good-tempered moody lovely amazing

25. **obedient**   obey defy giddy rebellious

26. **probable**   definite impossible unlikely rare

END OF TEST

/ 26

Time for a break! This puzzle is a great way to practise your **word-making** skills.

Fun Facts

Four friends are asked three questions about themselves. The answers they give are in the blue boxes on the right. Decide which person gave which answer based on their clues. Then fill in the profile for each person below.

What kind of pet do you have?
Charlotte: "My pet has four legs."
Billy: "My pet is a lot larger than Charlotte's and Matt's."
Matt: "My pet doesn't have fur."
Nora: "My pet can fly."

> Goldfish, Parrot
> Hamster, Rabbit

What is your favourite subject?
Charlotte: "I'm creative. I used to like History."
Billy: "Geography is boring and Maths is hard."
Matt: "I can't do Maths and I'm bad at drawing."
Nora: "I can't draw. I used to like Geography."

> Maths, History
> Geography, Art

What is your favourite hobby?
Charlotte: "I like to do my hobby on the way to school."
Billy: "I can do my hobby in my living room."
Matt: "I don't own a bike."
Nora: "I am not an outdoors person."

> Surfing, Cycling
> Knitting, Baking

Charlotte
Pet: _____
Subject: _____
Hobby: _____

Billy
Pet: _____
Subject: _____
Hobby: _____

Matt
Pet: _____
Subject: _____
Hobby: _____

Nora
Pet: _____
Subject: _____
Hobby: _____

You have **10 minutes** to do this test. Work as quickly and as accurately as you can.

Read this poem carefully and answer the questions that follow.

John the Swan

There was a lake not far from here,
Where every duck quivered in fear.
No quack could be heard, only shushes,
As mothers ushered their ducklings in bushes.

5   Once a watery city of ducks and geese,
Their lively lake turned to an eerie peace.
Whenever ripples appeared on the water
Griselda the Goose sheltered her daughter.

John the Swan's reign of terror,
10 Began after a terrible error.
Last summer he'd planned a holiday
To over the hills and far away.

With five grey cygnets* all in tow*,
He was all packed up and ready to go.
15 He called the cygnets with a quack.
No reply, nothing, no answer back.

His feathery children were sadly missing,
Furious honks followed mournful* hissing.
Understandably angry, beak in a scowl,
20 Taking it out on his neighbouring fowl.

When the humans came with bread,
It was always he who got ahead.
The other birds never got a crust,
They only approached if they must.

25 Then, one day, John's squawk was cheery.
No-one could believe what they were hearing.
Usually in his misery he'd be wallowing,
But, behind him, five grey swans were following.

Whispered rumours 'Where have they been?'
30 Perhaps they'd returned to their owner, the Queen?
Turns out they'd just arrived back, travelling east,
They'd gone to Canada, thinking they were geese.

*cygnet — *a young swan*
*in tow — *following behind*
*mournful — *very sad*

Answer these questions about the text that you've just read. Circle the letter that matches the correct answer.

1. What was the lake like before John lost his cygnets?

   A   Busy

   B   Quiet

   C   Lovely

   D   Dangerous

2. Why are the other birds scared?

   A   In case their children go missing

   B   Because John the Swan is angry

   C   All the swans are being mean

   D   The weather is treacherous

3. What was John doing when his cygnets went missing?

   A   Looking for food

   B   Sheltering in a bush

   C   Getting ready to go on holiday

   D   Flying over a hill

4. Why don't the other birds eat any bread?

   A   They prefer pondweed.

   B   The children only want to feed swans.

   C   They are afraid of John.

   D   They are always hiding in bushes.

5. Where had the five cygnets gone?
   A   Over the hills and far away
   B   Canada
   C   They were hiding in the lake.
   D   To see the Queen

6. What does "quivered" (line 2) mean?
   A   Hid
   B   Lived
   C   Swam
   D   Shook

7. What does "eerie" (line 6) mean?
   A   Strange
   B   Calm
   C   Hidden
   D   Pleasant

Find the word that means the same, or nearly the same, as the word on the left.

Example: **wide**   flat   straight   <u>broad</u>   long

8. **scrap**   metal   cut   stump   shred

9. **job**   office   hire   business   task

10. **con**   mock   man   cheat   truth

11. **fashionable**   favoured appreciated trendy pricey

12. **likelihood**   possibility able change definitely

13. **pledge**   honest declare announce promise

14. cheese milk cream ketchup butter

15. helicopter tractor bird aeroplane butterfly

16. werewolf supernatural vampire zombie ghost

17. tired weary sleepy fatigued bored

18. ant butterfly lobster ladybird fly

19. puzzled shocked confused baffled flummoxed

20. veranda balcony bungalow patio terrace

END OF TEST

/ 20

You have **10 minutes** to do this test. Work as quickly and as accurately as you can.

Read this passage carefully and answer the questions that follow.

An adapted extract from 'The Lamplighter'

Gerty knew no-one could see her and this gave her courage. She was gazing at Nan. Her eyes glistened with a fire of angry passion — a fire that Nan had lit long ago and which had not yet gone out. Now, seeing Nan made her anger come back to her in full force. Willie, thinking it was time to go home, left Gerty, saying, "Come
5 on, Gerty, I can't wait."

Gerty turned, saw that he was going, then, quick as lightning, bent down, and picking up a stone, flung it at the window. There was a crash of broken glass and Nan cried out, but Gerty was not there to see what had happened. The instant she heard the crash her fear returned, and flying past Willie, she didn't stop until she was
10 safe by True's side.

Willie didn't overtake them until they were nearly home, and then came running up, exclaiming, breathlessly, "Gerty, do you know what you did? You broke the window!"

Gerty jerked her shoulders from side to side to brush Willie off, pouted, and
15 declared that was what she meant to do.

True asked, "What window?" And Gerty confessed what she had done and that she did it on purpose. True and Willie were shocked and silent. Gerty was silent too for the rest of the walk. There were clouds on her face and she felt unhappy in her heart.

Maria S. Cummins

79

Answer these questions about the text that you've just read.
Circle the letter that matches the correct answer.

1. Why does Gerty throw a rock at the window?

    A   She is reminded of her anger towards Nan.

    B   She is aiming to hit the door.

    C   She is overexcited and cheerful.

    D   She doesn't want to go home with Willie.

2. Why didn't Gerty see what happened after she smashed the window?

    A   She closed her eyes.

    B   It was too dark to see.

    C   She was not close enough to the window.

    D   She had run off down the street.

3. What impression does Gerty want to give Willie after she's smashed the window?

    A   That she does not care about what she has done.

    B   That she is pleased about what she has done.

    C   That she has not done anything wrong.

    D   That Willie was lying.

4. How do Willie and True react to Gerty smashing the window?

    A   They are stunned.

    B   They are pleased.

    C   They are angry.

    D   They are happy.

5. How is Gerty feeling at the end of the passage?

    A   Relieved

    B   Pleased

    C   Upset

    D   Unsure

6. What does "courage" (line 1) mean?

    A   Noisiness

    B   Bravery

    C   Fury

    D   Energy

7. What does "confessed" (line 16) mean?

    A   Promised

    B   Refused

    C   Confided

    D   Admitted

Rearrange the words so that each sentence makes sense.
Underline the word which doesn't fit into the sentence.

Example: to I have <u>lamp</u> room my tidy

8.   cousin at library books my works the

9.   dog next barking kept door the bit

10. Ryan's and friend Switzerland moving was to

11. they opening a theatre are new is

12. mouldy gone carrots all rot have those

13. caretaker told cleans us school the off

14. jumps fence the over but quickly horse the

The words on the left are related in some way. Choose the word from the brackets that fits best with the words on the left.

Example: **car bus ferry coach** (road drive <u>train</u> cargo journey)

15. **annoy bother nag pester** (cheer worry sadden irritate livid)

16. **fad frenzy trend fashion** (tendency fan admire enjoy craze)

17. **rowing sailing canoeing rafting** (kayaking diving swim sails boat)

18. **campsite inn hostel chalet** (town beach hotel holiday airport)

19. **harbour dock jetty quay** (port ship anchor submarine ocean)

20. **jump bound hop spring** (trip leap sprint fly throw)

END OF TEST

/ 20

You have **10 minutes** to do this test. Work as quickly and as accurately as you can.

Choose the correct words to complete the passage below.

High in the mountains of Peru lies Machu Picchu — a

1. ☐ ruined
   ☐ hurt   city of dry-stone
   ☐ unbuilt

walls. It was built in the 1400s by the Incan Empire, a group of people

2. ☐ although
   ☐ where
   ☐ who

lived along the western coast of South America before Spanish explorers

3. ☐ destroyed
   ☐ come   .
   ☐ arrived

4. ☐ Unlike
   ☐ Also   many Incan cities, which were destroyed by the Spanish, Machu
   ☐ Maybe

5. ☐ remains
Picchu   ☐ contains   somewhat intact. It is thought that the city's remote location
   ☐ existed

6. ☐ means
   ☐ meant   that the Spanish invaders didn't know it existed. Historians are
   ☐ meaning

7. ☐ learn   8. ☐ high
   ☐ known   why a city was built so   ☐ long   up in the mountains. Some think it
   ☐ unsure   ☐ away

was where the Incan emperor went on holiday, and some think it was a religious site.

Although local people had always been
9. ☐ aware
☐ known   of the city, it was
☐ near

10. ☐ mystery
☐ ancient   to Westerners until 1911. An American archaeologist, Hiram Bingham,
☐ unknown

is credited with bringing the
11. ☐ Peru
☐ site   to the world's attention. However, there is
☐ people

evidence that other Westerners had already
12. ☐ visiting
☐ visit   the site in the 1800s.
☐ visited

Underline the word below that means the opposite,
or nearly the opposite, of the word on the left.

Example: **ill**   nice   <u>well</u>   sick   happy

13. **wonky**   shaky   still   level   wobbly

14. **impractical**   physical   useful   useless   awkward

15. **awake**   attention   tired   asleep   bored

16. **despair**   misery   anxiety   interest   hope

The words on the left are related in some way. Choose the word from the brackets that fits best with the words on the left.

Example: **car bus ferry coach** (road drive <u>train</u> cargo journey)

17. **kitten cub puppy foal** (chicken fox calf cow cat)

18. **porridge cereal pancakes yoghurt** (breakfast meal toast burger butter)

19. **troop pack flock shoal** (animal mass herd family sheep)

20. **chimp monkey orangutan baboon** (forest rat animal gorilla squirrel)

21. **cinema gallery zoo museum** (hall bank tourist theatre travel)

Complete the word on the right so that it means the same, or nearly the same, as the word on the left.

Example: foe

22. belief ⬚ a i t ⬚

23. guard p r ⬚ t e ⬚ t

24. summon ⬚ e c k ⬚ ⬚

25. fire ⬚ ⬚ a z e

26. crucial n ⬚ c ⬚ s s a ⬚ ⬚

END OF TEST

/ 26

85

Test 22

Time for a break! These puzzles are a great way to practise your **word-making** skills.

Rearranged Riddles

Two words in each sentence below have been swapped. Write down the swapped words, then rearrange the first letter of each word to answer the riddle.

I have plan cunning a to steal the pies. _____ _____

The beetle scuttled old the across map. _____ _____

The owl screeched inside from noisily the tree. _____ _____

I have many keys, but I can't open a single door. What am I?

I am _____.

Word Worm

How many words can you make from the letters in the word worm? Each letter must only be used once per word and each word must be at least three letters long. Hidden in the worm is a nine-letter word.

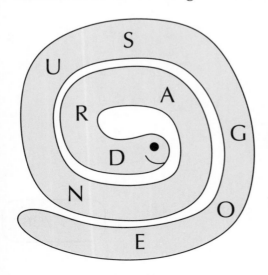

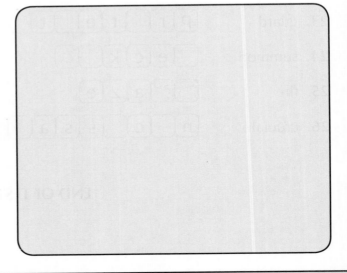

You have **10 minutes** to do this test. Work as quickly and as accurately as you can.

Fill in the missing letters to complete the words in the following passage.

1. There are thirteen d [ ] f f [ ] r e [ ] [ ] species of otter, and they can

2. be found [ ] c r [ ] s s the world and on nearly every continent.

3. They can be seen [ ] w i [ ] m i n [ ] in the rivers and streams of the

4. UK, where they h u [ ] [ ] for fish. Many of the habitats where otters live

5. were polluted with chemicals, and otters completely d i [ ] [ ] out in many

6. counties. Now, however, the number of otters is on the r [ ] s [ ], because

7. many of the h [ ] r m f [ ] [ ] chemicals have been banned.

8. One species of otter, the sea otter, lives almost [ ] n t [ ] r e [ ] y

9. in the ocean. They have the t h [ ] [ ] k e [ ] t fur of any animal. They

10. also cleverly use rocks to break [ ] p e [ ] the shells of sea creatures. Like

11. their river-dwelling cousins, the sea otter population had [ ] a l l e [ ],

12. but is [ ] [ ] w recovering again.

Find the word that means the same, or nearly the same, as the word on the left.

Example: **wide**   flat   straight   <u>broad</u>   long

13. **perhaps**   definitely   alright   impossible   maybe

14. **snooze**   lie   sniff   doze   laze

15. **dreadful**   excellent   mediocre   bearable   terrible

16. **aim**   point   skill   rude   jab

17. **joy**   delight   pleasant   sadness   worry

Four of the words in each list are linked. Underline the word that is **not** related to the other four.

Example: cow   hen   sheep   pig   <u>monkey</u>

18. tremble   swing   quiver   quake   shudder

19. soldier   policeman   uncle   mayor   firefighter

20. exhausted   overtired   overworked   fatigued   bothered

21. wind   sleet   hail   snow   rain

22. zoo   forest   jungle   desert   mountain

Rearrange the words so that each sentence makes sense.
Underline the word which doesn't fit into the sentence.

Example: to I have <u>lamp</u> room my tidy

23. ate felt scoff sick doughnuts ten Ken and

24. asked wash my cleaning me to up mum

25. bought grandmother present some Junaid his flowers

26. go to Neil we Sunday see should

END OF TEST

/ 26

You have **10 minutes** to do this test. Work as quickly and as accurately as you can.

Choose the correct words to complete the passage below.

1. ☐ lie
The Shetland Islands   ☐ lying   at the northernmost tip of the British Isles.
☐ lied

2. ☐ similar
Their landscape is   ☐ different   anywhere else in the UK. The islands are
☐ unlike

3. ☐ very   4. ☐ exactly
☐ incredible   bare, as there are   ☐ almost   no trees.
☐ huge   ☐ completely

5. ☐ came
Shetland ponies are a breed of pony which originally   ☐ bred   from the
☐ found

6. ☐ tall
islands. They are very small, usually under 1 metre   ☐ size   . The horses' size
☐ height

7. ☐ choice   8. ☐ made
makes them a good   ☐ riding   for children. They are also   ☐ thought   for
☐ horses   ☐ known

being gentle and good-natured. However, Shetland ponies have to be strong and tough

9. ☐ due
    ☐ because   of the harsh weather on the islands.
    ☐ despite

10. ☐ looked
Lots of wildlife can be   ☐ liked   off the coast of the Shetlands. People take
    ☐ seen

11. ☐ many
boats to spot a variety of animals   ☐ including   puffins, seals and killer whales.
    ☐ such

12. ☐ possible
Although the Shetland Islands are remote and   ☐ difficult   to reach, about 60,000
    ☐ better

tourists visit each year.

> Rearrange the words so that each sentence makes sense.
> Underline the word which doesn't fit into the sentence.
>
> **Example:**   to I have <u>lamp</u> room my tidy

13. not   seen   yesterday   in   I've   three   Lindsay   weeks

14. coat   on   gate   his   caught   rip   got   the

15. was   missed   minutes   the   train   late   fifteen

16. from   a   hurts   sore   Tim   leg   was   suffering

Four of the words in each list are linked. Underline the word that is **not** related to the other four.

Example: cow   hen   sheep   pig   <u>monkey</u>

17. ruler   headteacher   king   monarch   emperor

18. ostrich   budgie   canary   cockatoo   parrot

19. trifle   sorbet   sundae   cheesecake   dessert

20. imply   hint   suggest   indicate   show

21. convince   persuade   prevent   convert   sway

The words on the left are related in some way. Choose the word from the brackets that fits best with the words on the left.

Example: **car   bus   ferry   coach** (road   drive   <u>train</u>   cargo   journey)

22. **skyscraper   steeple   turret   spire** (church   warehouse   office   tower   high)

23. **nose   mouth   ear   hair** (cheek   toe   lung   elbow   shoulder)

24. **quarrel   debate   disagree   argue** (think   squabble   speak   talk   shout)

25. **live   lodge   dwell   inhabit** (remain   keep   apartment   burrow   reside)

26. **soft   spongy   mushy   doughy** (squashy   crispy   crunchy   firm   dry)

END OF TEST

/ 26

You have **10 minutes** to do this test. Work as quickly and as accurately as you can.

Read this poem carefully and answer the questions that follow.

An adapted version of 'Block City'

What are you able to build with your blocks?
Castles and palaces, temples and docks.
Rain may keep raining and others go roam,
But I can be happy and building at home.

5 Let the sofa be mountains, the carpet be sea,
There I'll establish a city for me:
A church and a mill and a palace beside,
And a harbour as well where my boats may ride.

Great is the palace with pillar and wall,
10 A sort of a tower on the top of it all,
And steps coming down in an orderly way
To where my toy boats lay safe in the bay.

This one is sailing and that one is moored:
Listen to the song of the sailors on board!
15 And see on the steps of my palace, the kings
Coming and going with presents and things!

20 Now I have done with it, down let it go!
All in a moment the town is laid low.
Block upon block lying scattered and free,
What is there left of my town by the sea?

Yet as I saw it, I see it again,
The church and the palace, the ships and the men,
And as long as I live and wherever I may be,
I'll always remember my town by the sea.

Robert Louis Stevenson

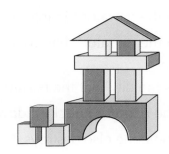

1. What does "go roam" (line 3) mean?

   A   Sail a ship

   B   Go for a walk

   C   Play football

   D   Go to school

2. Which of the following does the narrator not build out of blocks?

   A   Church

   B   Mountains

   C   Palace

   D   Mill

3. Where is the poem set?

   A   On a field

   B   In a strange city

   C   In the narrator's living room

   D   In the narrator's bathroom

4. Why does the city that the narrator has built disappear?

   A   The narrator knocks it down.

   B   Someone else destroys it.

   C   The rain knocks it down.

   D   The tower is too tall and falls down.

94

5. Which of the following statements is false?

    A   The narrator forgets about his city.

    B   There is a tower on top of the palace.

    C   There are steps leading from the palace to the bay.

    D   The city is very quickly destroyed.

6. What does "establish" (line 6) mean?

    A   Change

    B   Destroy

    C   Rebuild

    D   Set up

7. What does "orderly" (line 11) mean?

    A   Complicated

    B   Neat

    C   Confused

    D   Relaxed

Complete the word on the right so that it means the same, or nearly the same, as the word on the left.

Example: foe   [e][n][e][m][y]

---

8.   instruct   [c][o][m][ ][ ][n][d]

9.   remark   [c][ ][m][ ][e][ ][t]

10. house   [ ][c][c][ ][m][m][ ][d][ ][t][e]

11. sufficient   e ☐ o ☐ g h

12. odd   p ☐ c ☐ l i a ☐

13. caution   w ☐ r ☐ i ☐ g

Underline the word below that means the opposite,
or nearly the opposite, of the word on the left.

Example: **ill**   nice   <u>well</u>   sick   happy

---

14. **straighten**   shake   curl   flatten   flicker

15. **unusual**   rare   new   common   special

16. **panicked**   untroubled   asleep   furious   lazy

17. **secret**   lie   cheat   rumour   well-known

18. **dazzling**   sparkling   drab   black   glitter

19. **rude**   impolite   respectful   naughty   serious

20. **rushed**   unhurried   slow   noisy   slippy

END OF TEST

/ 20

Time for a break! These puzzles are a great way to practise your **logic** and **spelling** skills.

Football Thief

Guy's football was stolen from his garden on Sunday. Guy has drawn up a list of suspects in his diary and has asked them to say where they were at the time of the crime. He knows <u>one</u> of them is lying and stole the football. Work out who stole the football and explain how you did it.

Who stole Guy's football?

_____

How do you know?

_____

_____

•	Moussa: "I was alone in the library."
•	Stu: "I was at a birthday party."
•	Claire: "I was walking my dog."
•	Henry: "I was at school."
•	Louise: "I was playing netball."
•	Rupa: "I was at my uncle's house."

Top-Secret Treehouse

Each of the words below has one spelling mistake. Circle the incorrect letter in each word and write the correct letter in the numbered box. The correct letters give instructions on how to get into Imogen's secret treehouse.

1 d e s k r i b e

3 c o l u m m

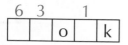
5 k a m e r a

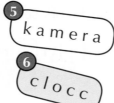
2 s i t u a s i o n

4 i n v y t e

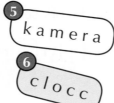
6 c l o c c

To get into Imogen's treehouse, you need to:

6	3		1		2		4	5
		o		k		w		e

⏱ 10

You have **10 minutes** to do this test. Work as quickly and as accurately as you can.

Fill in the missing letters to complete the words in the following passage.

1. Table tennis, or ping-pong, is a game that was i n v [ ] [ ] t [ ] d by the

2. Victorians. It used to be [ ] l [ ] y [ ] d with heavy golf balls and wooden

3. bats, but nowadays a [ ] i g h [ ] e [ ] plastic ball is used and the bats
   are covered with rubber.

4. The first World Table Tennis Championships [ ] o [ ] k place in London

5. in 1926 and the game b [ ] c a [ ] e an Olympic sport in 1988.

6. The [ ] o u [ ] t [ ] y where table tennis has been most popular is

7. China, where it is taken very [ ] e r i [ ] u s l [ ]. It was declared the

8. national sport in the 1950s and the m [ ] j [ ] r [ ] t y of schools have

9. teams that train regularly. Professional players train for at l [ ] a s [ ]

10. 7 hours a day and the Chinese team have [ ] n v [ ] n t [ ] d many new

11. techniques. All this hard work seems to have [ ] a i [ ] off! At the 2016 Rio

12. Olympic Games, China [ ] o [ ] every gold medal in table tennis.

The words on the left are related in some way. Choose the word from the brackets that fits best with the words on the left.

Example: **car bus ferry coach** (road drive <u>train</u> cargo journey)

13. **chilly nippy cool crisp** (snow warm sleet icy frost)

14. **milkshake smoothie cola cordial** (coffee juice tea drink yoghurt)

15. **peach cherry nectarine apricot** (plum coconut sweetcorn salad egg)

16. **bliss joy delight elation** (wonderful happiness satisfy splendid misery)

17. **astonish amaze astound stun** (bother annoy applaud surprise worry)

Four of the words in each list are linked. Underline the word that is **not** related to the other four.

Example: cow hen sheep pig <u>monkey</u>

18. blackcurrant pear strawberry blueberry raspberry

19. stench stink scent aroma flavour

20. mile metre inch distance centimetre

21. explode clang chime ring jangle

22. racket bat paddle club ball

Find the word that means the same, or nearly the same, as the word on the left.

Example: **wide**   flat   straight   <u>broad</u>   long

23. **swell**   pop   explode   expand   hurt

24. **portion**   helping   entire   dinner   rationing

25. **determined**   organise   stubborn   ambition   decide

26. **sketch**   draft   project   final   invent

END OF TEST

/ 26

You have **10 minutes** to do this test. Work as quickly and as accurately as you can.

Choose the correct words to complete the passage below.

Many animal species that currently live
1. ☐ far
☐ during
☐ throughout
Europe (such as beavers,

wild boar and wolves)
2. ☐ existed
☐ lived
☐ disappeared
from Britain a long time ago — sadly many of

these species were hunted to extinction.

In
3. ☐ ages
☐ ancient
☐ previously
times, most of Britain would have been covered in

woodland, but
4. ☐ nowadays
☐ afterwards
☐ beforehand
only around 13% of Britain is forest. Rewilding

Britain is a charity
5. ☐ dedicated
☐ tries
☐ aimed
to bringing Britain's forests
6. ☐ alive
☐ here , as well as
☐ back

reintroducing many of the species that had died
7. ☐ over
☐ in .
☐ out

8. ☐ According
   ☐ Saying   to Rewilding Britain, there are
   ☐ Because

9. ☐ hundreds
   ☐ several   benefits to growing
   ☐ lots

forests. One of the most important is that trees

10. ☐ provide
    ☐ create   us with clean air to breathe.
    ☐ give

However, farmers don't always agree with those people who

11. ☐ support
    ☐ enjoy
    ☐ favourable

rewilding. They are

12. ☐ pleased
    ☐ worried   that predators such as wolves would eat their animals.
    ☐ terrifying

Complete the word on the right so that it means the opposite,
or nearly the opposite, of the word on the left.

Example: strong   [w][e][a][k]

13. clueless   [ ][i][s][ ]

14. simple   [e][l][ ][b][ ][r][ ][t][e]

15. firm   [f][l][ ][ ][i][b][ ][e]

16. gorgeous   [ ][i][d][e][ ][ ][s]

The words on the left are related in some way. Choose the word from the brackets that fits best with the words on the left.

Example: **car bus ferry coach** (road drive <u>train</u> cargo journey)

17. **desire longing passion yearning** (favourite eager keen craving enjoy)

18. **calm cool tranquil serene** (slow steady peaceful free agitated)

19. **agony suffering torment woe** (pain pleasure annoyance fury wound)

20. **ladle grater spatula peeler** (cheese whisk oven cooking baking)

21. **star meteor asteroid comet** (space alien planet rocket spaceship)

Four of the words in each list are linked. Underline the word that is **not** related to the other four.

Example: cow hen sheep pig <u>monkey</u>

22. cobra chameleon python viper rattlesnake

23. slurp chew nibble gnaw munch

24. staffroom classroom hall homework playground

25. vicar believer priest monk nun

26. glass rock stone boulder pebble

END OF TEST

/ 26

Test 28

You have **10 minutes** to do this test. Work as quickly and as accurately as you can.

Read this passage carefully and answer the questions that follow.

Tim Peake

In December 2015, Tim Peake, from Chichester, became the first British astronaut to go to the International Space Station. Not only that, but he also made history by becoming the first British person ever to do a spacewalk — to get out of the spacecraft while in orbit.*

5   While in the space station, Tim did a number of live video linkups with children across the UK. It is thought that around a million British children have taken part in experiments at school inspired by Tim's mission, setting off a wave of enthusiasm for science and maths subjects. In the past, there had been a lack of students studying these subjects. However, that trend has begun to reverse and it is hoped that after

10 Tim's mission even more people will be inspired to take them up.

During his descent in June 2016, Tim's capsule travelled at around 17,000 mph. Travelling at such high speed creates immense levels of friction and heat. Once a capsule has come back down to Earth it can't be used again. Tim's capsule has been on display at the Science Museum in London, still covered in burn marks from

15 his return trip to Earth. Another exhibition entirely devoted to his journey has been opened in his hometown.

Although he has been called "Britain's first astronaut", the title is not entirely accurate. In 1991, Helen Sharman, a chemist from Sheffield, flew to the Russian Mir Space Station after having won a competition. She set off from the same spaceport

20 and in the same type of capsule as Tim.

*in orbit — *rotating around the Earth*

Answer these questions about the text that you've just read.
Circle the letter that matches the correct answer.

1. According to the text, what effect has Tim Peake had on British children?

   A   More British children want to become astronauts.

   B   More British children have visited the Science Museum in London.

   C   More British children have an interest in science and maths.

   D   British children want more video linkups in their lessons.

2. Which of the following best describes Tim Peake?

   A   The first Briton in space

   B   The first chemist in space

   C   The first Briton to go to the moon

   D   The first Briton to have done a spacewalk

3. Approximately how long was Tim in space for?

   A   Six months

   B   A year

   C   Three years

   D   Two weeks

4. Why did Tim's capsule have burn marks?

   A   It had already been into space.

   B   There had been an accident.

   C   It was scorched on the way back down to Earth.

   D   There was a fire at the exhibition.

5. According to the text, which of the following must be true?

   A   Tim Peake inspired one million more people to study science or maths.

   B   Tim Peake only studied science and maths.

   C   Around one million children were involved in live video linkups.

   D   Tim Peake inspired experiments in many British schools.

6. Which of the following do Tim Peake and Helen Sharman have in common?

   A   They are from the same town.

   B   They are both chemists.

   C   They both set off from the same spaceport.

   D   They both did a spacewalk.

7. Where has the exhibition about Tim's journey opened?

   A   In many places across the UK

   B   London

   C   Sheffield

   D   Chichester

Four of the words in each list are linked. Underline the word that is **not** related to the other four.

Example: cow   hen   sheep   pig   <u>monkey</u>

---

8. carpenter   electrician   receptionist   decorator   plumber

9. dragon   spider   ogre   unicorn   phoenix

10. doctor   dame   lord   duke   princess

11. radio   programme   computer   television   stereo

12. email message postman letter postcard

13. knee wrist elbow heart ankle

14. perfume shampoo aftershave deodorant fragrance

The words on the left are related in some way. Choose the word from the brackets that fits best with the words on the left.

Example: **car bus ferry coach** (road drive <u>train</u> cargo journey)

15. **pot sieve wok colander** (kitchen toaster spices pan recipe)

16. **chisel saw mallet spanner** (workshop tools bench scissors hammer)

17. **grandma aunt niece daughter** (uncle brother family woman mother)

18. **comb hairdryer bobble hairclip** (soap ponytail hairbrush bob tangled)

19. **mop sponge hoover brush** (bleach broom clean dust toothpaste)

20. **pasty strudel tart croissant** (meat bakery sandwich potato pie)

END OF TEST

/ 20

Test 28

Time for a break! These puzzles are a great way to practise your **word-making** skills.

Word Maze

Draw a line from the grey letter through the word maze to the opposite side. You can only follow paths that spell out a word that is similar in meaning to 'succeed'. You can only walk on each square once.

```
E V A I L P R E P A R E A P T I S H O T O U R S
R       R       E       A       U       T       L       I
P R O M   O D U C A D V E R S Q   H       F   S H
E       O   S       H       A       N       R       E   A
V       T   P       P       N   S V A N I S H M A K E
E       E   E       M       C   S       V       O       T
I       F   R T R I U M E R E   S P E C T C Y C L
H       L   A       A       R       M       R   U
A C T I O N I   P M O C C   G O R   A D D E N R E
C       U   S   L       T       P   S       V   T
E P T N D E R I S H F U L F I L S T E R O B S H
```

Word Match

Use one word or group of letters from each column to make as many words as you can.

mis	interest	er	unlocked
re	inform	ment	
un	lock	ing	
dis	pay	ed	

You have **10 minutes** to do this test. Work as quickly and as accurately as you can.

Fill in the missing letters to complete the words in the following passage.

1. Elizabeth Fry was ☐o☐r☐ in 1780 in Norwich. Although her family were

2. rich, she was interested in helping the poor and s☐☐k. In 1813, she

3. visited Newgate Prison in London and was h☐r r☐f☐e d by

4. what she saw. The prison was overcrowded and children l☐☐e d

5. there, just because their mothers were c☐i m☐☐a l s.

6. Prisoners slept on straw on the f l☐☐r in tiny, dirty cells. Elizabeth

7. brought them ☐l e a☐ clothes and food. She set up a school for

8. children and taught the women prisoners how to sew and ☐☐a d. She

9. influenced o☐☐e r people to make prison conditions better and was

10. hugely admired in her time. T☐a n☐s to her work, conditions in

11. many prisons i☐p r☐v e☐. There was a picture of Elizabeth on

12. the five-pound ☐o☐e between 2002-2017.

Four of the words in each list are linked. Underline the word that is **not** related to the other four.

Example: cow hen sheep pig <u>monkey</u>

13. surgeon patient nurse midwife paramedic

14. blurred clouded brightened obscured muddied

15. spaniel puppy husky bulldog Labrador

16. clover dandelion daisy buttercup leaf

17. explore ignore examine investigate probe

The words on the left are related in some way. Choose the word from the brackets that fits best with the words on the left.

Example: **car bus ferry coach** (road drive <u>train</u> cargo journey)

18. **sword axe dagger crossbow** (knight soldier battle spear horse)

19. **track field court rink** (pitch sport athletics ball net)

20. **freezer stove oven dishwasher** (dining storage cooking cool fridge)

21. **bucket spade flip-flops sunscreen** (sea sand sunglasses beach shell)

22. **trousers leggings skirt underpants** (vest gown jeans shirt suit)

Complete the word on the right so that it means the opposite, or nearly the opposite, of the word on the left.

Example: strong [w][e][a][k]

23. give   [r][e][ ][ ][ ][v][e]

24. learn   [ ][e][a][ ][h]

25. formal   [c][ ][s][ ][a][l]

26. real   [i][m][ ][g][ ][n][ ][r][y]

END OF TEST

/ 26

You have **10 minutes** to do this test. Work as quickly and as accurately as you can.

Read this passage carefully and answer the questions that follow.

An adapted extract from 'Erick and Sally'

As Sally had been used to doing, she now ran right into the house. After entering the front door, she stood in the small kitchen and was at once in front of another door which led into the living-room. This door stood wide open and Sally found herself suddenly in the presence of a lady dressed in black, who sat in that room sewing and
5 who lifted her head at Sally's noisy entrance. With large sad eyes, she looked at the child in silence.

Sally grew as red as fire and in her embarrassment remained standing near the door like she was rooted to the floor.

Now the lady held out her hand and said in a friendly tone, "Come here, dear
10 child, what brings you to me?"

She approached the lady and wanted to say something, but nothing came out. Sally grew crimson and stood there more helpless than ever before in her life.
The lady took the child's hand and stroked her glowing cheeks.

"Come, sit down beside me, dear child," she then said, with a voice so sweet that
15 it went deep into Sally's heart. "Come, we will gradually get to know each other a little."

Now there came from out of a corner a quick noise of moving. Sally did not know what it was, for until now she had not dared to look around the room, but now she looked up.

20 A boy, a little taller than she, was carrying a small chair and placed it before Sally. He looked at her with such a merry face as the restrained laughter came so visibly out of his eyes that the sight brought a complete transformation in Sally's feelings, and she, all at once, laughed out loud.

Johanna Spyri

Answer these questions about the text that you've just read.
Circle the letter that matches the correct answer.

1. Sally is described as having grown "as red as fire" (line 7). What does this mean?

   A   She was wearing too much makeup.

   B   She was about to cry.

   C   She was sunburnt.

   D   She was incredibly embarrassed.

2. What does the woman do when Sally runs into the house?

   A   She shouts at Sally.

   B   She tells her to get out.

   C   She says that they should get to know each other.

   D   She offers her a drink.

3. How does Sally feel when the woman begins talking to her on line 9?

   A   Confident

   B   Upset

   C   Uncomfortable

   D   Courageous

4. Why does Sally start laughing?

   A   The woman makes her feel more comfortable.

   B   The boy looks so cheerful that she feels cheerful too.

   C   The boy looks funny, which makes her laugh.

   D   She feels so awkward that she starts laughing.

5. Which of the following statements must be true?

    A   The woman is wearing a red dress.

    B   The front door leads into the kitchen.

    C   Sally sees the boy straight away.

    D   The woman is sitting in the kitchen.

6. What does "helpless" (line 12) mean?

    A   Unable

    B   Powerful

    C   Terrible

    D   Capable

7. What does "transformation" (line 22) mean?

    A   Mixture

    B   Opposite

    C   Movement

    D   Change

Underline the word below that means the opposite, or nearly the opposite, of the word on the left.

    Example: ill   nice <u>well</u> sick happy

8. **shy**   timid satisfying daring reckless

9. **uncover**   lie hide reveal secret

10. **straightforward**   easy amazing boring complex

11. **inexact**   absolutely definitely precise obvious

12. **unique**   few different typical only

13. **below**   across away above high

Rearrange the words so that each sentence makes sense.
Underline the word which doesn't fit into the sentence.

Example: to I have <u>lamp</u> room my tidy

---

14. ages took drove to it France to get

15. holidays the Spain spend we in swim

16. was stayed Greg went in sick so bed

17. built school a builds new is being

18. in hid tortoise the walk its shell

19. loved pears cheese eat to Rani sandwiches

20. played with cricket on beach the they

END OF TEST

/ 20

115

Test 31

You have **10 minutes** to do this test. Work as quickly and as accurately as you can.

Choose the correct words to complete the passage below.

The Day of the Dead is a festival which is
1. ☐ happening
   ☐ celebrated   in late October and
   ☐ taken

2. ☐ all
   ☐ entire   November in Mexico. Although it
   ☐ early

3. ☐ sounds
   ☐ appears   like a sad occasion,
   ☐ is

the holiday is
4. ☐ misery
   ☐ joyful   . Mexicans celebrate the lives of those who have died,
   ☐ upset

5. ☐ instead
   ☐ rather   than focusing on their deaths. The traditions are very old and
   ☐ better

6. ☐ exist
   ☐ arise
   ☐ date

back to before Europeans came to Mexico. Families create temporary altars to honour

their
7. ☐ loved
   ☐ former   ones. They display pictures of deceased family
   ☐ best

8. ☐ relative
   ☐ people
   ☐ members

alongside candles, water and marigold flowers. Sugar skulls are
9. ☐ made
   ☐ bake   for
   ☐ designing

116

the festival — these are small skulls made out of sugar and

10. ☐ bright
    ☐ colours   decorated.
    ☐ colourfully

11. ☐ Popular
    ☐ Another   symbol of the festival is a female skeleton called Catrina. She was first
    ☐ Only

12. ☐ created
    ☐ drew   by the artist José Guadalupe Posada.
    ☐ inventing

The words on the left are related in some way. Choose the word from the brackets that fits best with the words on the left.

Example: **car bus ferry coach** (road drive <u>train</u> cargo journey)

13. **ballet tap salsa foxtrot** (waltz dance perform opera sing)

14. **highchair buggy dummy cot** (wheelchair pram baby child nursery)

15. **novel dictionary textbook cookbook** (letter write thesaurus read poem)

16. **beige turquoise crimson pink** (colour paint bright violet rainbow)

17. **Spain France Italy Russia** (London capital Germany Europe country)

Four of the words in each list are linked. Underline the word that is **not** related to the other four.

Example: cow hen sheep pig <u>monkey</u>

18. irritated furious livid enraged seething

19. October Autumn May August February

20. moustache eyelash eyebrow eyelid beard

21. tangy spicy peppery plain hot

22. biscuits rice pasta bread noodles

Find the word that means the same, or nearly the same, as the word on the left.

Example: **wide** flat straight <u>broad</u> long

23. **remote** near distant rural alone

24. **wreck** build ship sink ruin

25. **certainly** very clear definite absolutely

26. **total** whole add part everything

END OF TEST

/ 26

V4XPDE1